MW00606285

GENERATION GREEN: The Making of the UniverCity Childcare Centre

Ecotone Publishing — an Imprint of International Living Future Institute

For more information write:

Ecotone Publishing
721 NW Ninth Avenue, Suite 195
Portland, OR 97209

Author: Michael Berrisford
Book Design: softfirm
Edited by: Fred McLennan
Primary Photography by: Martin Tessler

Library of Congress Control Number: 2013949824
Library of Congress Cataloging-in Publication Data

ISBN 978-0-9826902-7-7

1. ARCHITECTURE   2. ENVIRONMENT   3. PHILOSOPHY

First Edition

Printed in Canada on Reincarnation Matte paper — one hundred percent recycled content, processed chlorine free, using vegetable-based ink.

GENERATION GREEN

The Making of the
UniverCity Childcare Centre

LIVING
BUILDING
CHALLENGE

TABLE OF CONTENTS

FOREWORD

The greenest childcare centre on the planet began its life on the top floor of a six-storey parking garage.

Really, that was the plan. Regardless that SFU Community Trust was established to develop a model sustainable community next to Simon Fraser University's campus on Burnaby Mountain, the original plan was to build a 1,400-car parking garage in the very heart of our walkable and transit-oriented community. Given that the Trust also had committed to the City of Burnaby to build a childcare centre, the need for affordable space triggered the unusual solution: stack one project on top of the other. The rooftop site would make room for a childcare centre that met minimum health and safety requirements, and we hoped that, with a little care and attention, we might be able to achieve a LEED Silver construction standard. Admittedly, the goal was not very ambitious.

Nor was it much of a good idea. In 2007, when we took a good look at the parkade economics, we recognized that it was a loser — monetarily as well as morally. Good planning meant there would never be enough cars in the neighbourhood to justify its existence.

Still, I was surprised — the day I persuaded the Board of Directors to kill the parkade — to have our Director of Development, Dale Mikkelsen, walk into my office and suggest that we take a high-value, high-visibility residential site, kitty-corner from a LEED Gold elementary school and across from a park, and build a childcare centre that would meet the Living Building Challenge. It was one of those crazy ideas that is too appealing to dismiss out of hand.

The first obstacle was the site: to free up the land, we convinced the City of Burnaby to allow us to transfer the residential density to an adjacent site.

But that left an even bigger challenge: we had a budget — the modest amount we had set aside to build a childcare centre on the roof of a parking garage. So I said to Dale, "If you can deliver a Living Building for that price, I'm all for it." And our Board of Directors agreed.

What followed was the kind of adventure that makes our work at SFU Community Trust so fun and so rewarding. We found a great architect (Karen Marler at Hughes Condon Marler Architects), a great builder (Ledcor Construction), and a great group of creative and resourceful suppliers and regulators. It was not easy — the best things never are — but when we opened the doors, we were on schedule and 18 percent below the cost of conventional childcare centres being built in Metro Vancouver at the same time. I was particularly gratified when International Living Future Institute founder and CEO Jason F. McLennan came to the opening ceremonies and called it "the greenest childcare centre on the planet."

This project was all the work of an extremely bright and enthusiastic team. I must particularly thank Dale Mikkelsen for the inspiration — and for the inspirational effort that he brought to the task. Thanks to Jason McLennan and the International Living Future Institute for setting a standard that is at once the highest in the land, but still sensible, practical and — we've proven it — achievable at a perfectly reasonable price. And

thanks as well for the time that he spent working with us to ensure we never lost sight of the goal and that we never became discouraged in the search for true sustainability. Thanks again to Karen Marler and Jeff Cutler at space2place landscape architects. And thank you to the SFU Childcare Society, to Executive Director Pat Frouws, a fabulous partner in the design and construction stages, and to Program Director Karen Vaughan, who manages a spectacular team of educators who deliver one of the most impressive childcare programs in the country.

In short, thanks to everyone involved in the project — all of whom found the time to do their jobs in a new, different and creative way. We have achieved something here that is proving itself worthy of worldwide attention and regard. I am truly grateful to all those who made it possible.

GORDON HARRIS
President and CEO
SFU Community Trust

3

ACKNOWLEDGEMENTS

I am very grateful to Jason F. McLennan for introducing me to his groundbreaking idea for "Living Buildings" back in 1999 when he and fellow architect/renowned thinker, Bob Berkebile, dared to dream of the built environment in terms of the elegance and efficiency inherent in nature's architecture. Ever since that time, I have been captivated by the far-reaching possibilities that the Living Building concept inspires and I have been enthusiastically following the Living Building phenomena professionally. And further, I am incredibly fortunate to have a career that allows me to document the most innovative developments in the green building movement. Witnessing Jason's pioneering idea germinate and grow to become a global movement with real, functioning, and wildly successful Living Buildings has been awe-inspiring.

I thank Gordon Harris and Dale Mikkelsen for boldly championing their vision for UniverCity, for their decision to take on the Living Building Challenge, and for generously sharing their time and experiences for this publication. I also offer sincere thanks to the remarkably dedicated and expert green design pioneers at Hughes Condon Marler Architects, especially Karen Marler, Kourosh Mahavash and Jay Lin, for granting me full access to their Living Building experience. Through HCMA, I discovered that the very best designers are lifelong learners, without ego, and still channel the imaginative powers of children. I am truly honored to be the storyteller connected to the revolutionary undertaking and ultimate achievement of the UniverCity Childcare Living Building.

My ongoing appreciation goes to Fred McLennan who always finds a way to ground my writing with insightful editing, shaping my contributions into articulations worthy of publishing. And, likewise, I extend my gratitude to the incredibly talented Erin Gehle and Johanna Björk for artfully transforming words into elegant collections of pages wrapped in compelling covers. What Fred does for words, Erin and Johanna do with design and I am genuinely thankful to have fitted somewhere in the middle for over nine years.

Finally, I give special, heartfelt thanks to my wife Melissa, and children, Haley, Holden and Connor for your unconditional and unwavering love and support. You are at the heart of why I think Living Buildings and Living Communities are so incredibly important.

MICHAEL D. BERRISFORD
2014

AUTHOR PROFILE

Michael D. Berrisford is the Director of Ecotone Publishing, a division of the International Living Future Institute and the Senior Editor of *Trim Tab*, the organization's quarterly transformative design magazine. Michael overseas the research, writing and production of Ecotone's ever-growing portfolio of innovative books on sustainable design, including the Living Building Challenge Series and the Green Masters Series.

Michael is a dedicated naturalist and environmental advocate. In his spare time he eagerly coaches triathlon and running to youth and the young at heart. He resides in the ecologically unique Okanagan Valley in British Columbia, Canada with his wife Melissa, daughter Haley and twin boys Connor and Holden.

PART I

Lofty Aspirations

Sound Plans for a Good Education

"A child's world is fresh and new and beautiful, full of wonder and excitement. It is our misfortune that for most of us that clear-eyed vision, that true instinct for what is beautiful and awe-inspiring, is dimmed and even lost before we reach adulthood. If I had influence with the good fairy who is supposed to preside over the christening of all children, I should ask that her gift to each child in the world be a sense of wonder so indestructible that it would last throughout life, as an unfailing antidote against the boredom and disenchantment of later years... the alienation from the sources of our strength."

RACHEL CARSON
The Sense of Wonder

HIGHER GROUND FOR DESIGN AND LEARNING

The profound significance of the setting of the UniverCity Childcare Centre is undeniable. Located in the geographic heart of Metro Vancouver, in what strives to be Canada's most sustainable new community, and adjacent to Simon Fraser University (SFU), one of the nation's finest educational institutions, one gets the distinct sense that something extraordinary is occurring on the upper reaches of Burnaby Mountain.

Situated high above British Columbia's beautiful Lower Mainland, within a natural, protected evergreen forest, SFU's UniverCity community looks out over a dynamic assembly of vibrant metropolitan activity set among stunning panoramic views of mountain slopes, coniferous forest, and deep inlets of the Pacific Ocean.

On a clear day, the green contours of Vancouver Island, the Gulf Islands and Discovery Islands are partially visible across the Georgia Strait to the west, lying well beyond the silvery steel-and-glass architecture of downtown Vancouver. The massive cinder cone of Washington State's snow-capped Mount Baker stands sentinel to the south. British Columbia's spectacular Burrard Inlet and the coastal mountains of Vancouver's emerald Northshore dominate the panorama to the north. This iconic natural capital has earned the region the reputation of being one of the most desirable locations on earth to live, work and play. The exceptional lifestyle opportunities of an ecotone *where water meets mountains* (farmer's market then cycle, paddle and alpine ski all in the same day) in a temperate climate is a highly desirable scenario for many. However, the region's abundant attributes, combined with

> *"Earth and sky, woods and fields, lakes and rivers, the mountain and the sea, are excellent schoolmasters, and teach some of us more than we can ever learn from books."*
>
> JOHN LUBBOCK

UniverCity, Burnaby, British Columbia

the robust commercial activity associated with British Columbia's tourism, diverse industries, agriculture, high-tech sector, natural resources, and a relative proximity to Pacific Rim economies, are some significant factors that have led to an elevated cost of living in this Pacific Northwest paradise.

UniverCity is an attractive, thoughtfully-planned community on Burnaby Mountain unlike any other. Designed purposefully to harmonize with the abundant natural beauty of British Columbia, planners have steadfastly abided by the visionary "Four Cornerstones of Sustainability" (Environment, Economy, Equity, Education) established by SFU. The burgeoning, life-style oriented development has become increasingly well-known for offering an increasing array of high-quality, stylish, relatively-affordable residential options and modern services befitting a sustainable, fully-functioning neighborhood.

Whether one's ascent to the top of Burnaby Mountain originates from below in bustling urban Burnaby, booming Surrey, the Tri-Cities, the Trans Canada Trail, or from any number of tranquil local footpaths emanating from the nearby ecologically-designed residences of the growing community, arriving here is impressive. There is a real possibility (and legitimate environmental case) that a high-speed gondola may someday efficiently service the mountaintop. Though by whatever means or mode, visitors cannot help but reach UniverCity primed with anticipation — curious about prospects of learning something about the intention of this unique place and of the all-important integrations between the inhabitants and the environment that have culminated in the creation of what may well be Canada's most sustainable community — and home of the *very first, "fully-certified"* Living Building in Canada — UniverCity Childcare Centre.

GENERATION GREEN

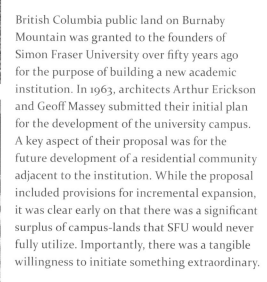

TOP: Altaire high-rise community
located in UniverCity Highlands

BOTTOM LEFT: Roof-Topping Ceremony:
Gordon Harris, David Gillanders, and Neil Chrystal

BOTTOM RIGHT: Town Square, UniverCity

SIMON FRASER UNIVERSITY
— THEN AND NOW

British Columbia public land on Burnaby Mountain was granted to the founders of Simon Fraser University over fifty years ago for the purpose of building a new academic institution. In 1963, architects Arthur Erickson and Geoff Massey submitted their initial plan for the development of the university campus. A key aspect of their proposal was for the future development of a residential community adjacent to the institution. While the proposal included provisions for incremental expansion, it was clear early on that there was a significant surplus of campus-lands that SFU would never fully utilize. Importantly, there was a tangible willingness to initiate something extraordinary.

In 1995, a Memorandum of Understanding was signed between then President of SFU, John Stubbs, and Mayor William Copeland of Burnaby, British Columbia. The forward-thinking collaboration resulted in 320 plus hectares of University-owned land being transferred to the City of Burnaby for inclusion in the Burnaby Mountain Conservation Area.

In exchange, SFU was given approval to begin planning and developing a mountaintop community now known as UniverCity. The Official Community Plan (OCP) and related Zoning Bylaw Amendments for a high-density, mixed-use community on approximately sixty-five hectares of land surrounding the campus was officially approved in 1996. The development parameters allowed for up to 4,536 residential housing units to be distributed through several neighborhoods located close to the university, and included specifications for a centralized commercial core, community facilities, urban parks, and elementary schools, all connected by an extensive network of pedestrian pathways and cycling trails. According to the OCP, the anticipated population of UniverCity was projected to number approximately ten thousand residents at full capacity. The land that was once deemed surplus to the needs of the university had been repurposed in a profound and meaningful way that would benefit citizens of British Columbia in perpetuity.

11

ESTABLISHING TRUST

UniverCity did not become a sustainable community overnight — people purposefully made it so.

The original proposal in the mid-1960s from Erickson and Massey envisioning a residential development in close proximity to the campus dovetailed nicely with the aspirations of the university to foster a robust educational culture for decades to come. And, as synergistic interactions and relationships are nature's methodology for a healthy ecosystem, SFU has honored Nature's example by establishing a prolific urban ecology on the mountain that was designed to function with deep respect for people and for place.

In 1997, the Burnaby Mountain Community Corporation was formed for the purpose of planning the new development. Now renamed and officially recognized as the SFU Community Trust (the Trust), the organization's primary responsibility is to direct the development

of the designated lands surrounding the institution. Established by SFU as a market-based development entity, today the Trust is governed by a highly qualified, well-rounded, independent Board of Directors and operated by a professional staff led by visionary CEO and President Gordon Harris and green design savvy Director of Development Dale Mikkelsen. Under the initial leadership of Michael Geller, a Community Advisory Committee comprised of a broad spectrum of stakeholders charged with providing representative feedback about the qualities and attributes they value for the community. Through the collaboration of these various groups, a Community Vision Statement was formalized, marking the commencement of the phase-based planning and design process to be implemented by the Trust.

The Hub, at UniverCity

NESTERS MARKET

Pharmacy

Part I: **LOFTY ASPIRATIONS**

"It's one of those idyllic business relationships that makes economic and environmental sense. Our green building requirements appeal to developers for their simplicity, clarity and certainty — and gives us something that simply does not exist anywhere else in North America."

DALE MIKKELSEN
Director of Development,
SFU Community Trust

RESPONSIBILITY AND SUSTAINABILITY

The Trust is responsible for carrying out the goals set forth by SFU, fundamentally operating in the role of "master developer" for UniverCity.

Specifically, the Trust is charged with the task of "Creating a complete community on Burnaby Mountain, with a diverse selection of housing and a full range of shops, services and amenities," and "Building an endowment fund to support teaching and research at SFU." Gordon Harris describes the role of the Trust another way, stating that "our structure serves as a bridge — the success of UniverCity leads to the well-being of SFU," referring to the contributions to the Endowment Fund garnered from profits gleaned from the development. Dale Mikkelsen distilled the role and responsibility of the Trust further stating, "Our job is to do well (financially) by doing good (sustainably)." The Trust staff and its allies have a very clear understanding of the goals that guide their actions. What is considered impressive are the high standards and principles connected to the environment, economy, equity, and education by which they have gone about creating a leading-edge

model of sustainable community building that educates and inspires at so many levels.

Through the judicious development of UniverCity, the Trust is well positioned to realize its mandate of creating a desirable, sustainable, mixed-use residential community while targeting a cumulative contribution of $150 million to the university's endowment fund by the time the community is completed. To date, the sustainable development model has been tremendously successful, endorsed by the avowal of the well over three thousand fulltime residents that now call UniverCity home. UniverCity has been a hybrid, high-performance vehicle for economic and societal change at SFU, already raising close to $30 million for research activities and education, fortifying the core academic structure, and adding valuable services for students and faculty in the process. In effect, the development has improved the quality of the university-community life overall.

University High Street is a hub of activity, with a bustling public plaza and convenient access to shopping, restaurants, and services.

URBAN DEVELOPMENT
IN BALANCE WITH NATURE

Nature tends to evolve toward relative equilibrium; in essence, what it needs to be in order to be healthy and successful. An ecosystem is generally defined as a community of living organisms existing together with non-living components of their environment (like air, water and soil); all parts interacting systematically. Functionally, living and non-living parts of a flourishing ecosystem are linked together through circles, cycles and energy flows.

This description of an ecosystem rings similar to the dynamic structure of organizations, groups, and inhabitants to which the UniverCity Childcare Centre is inter-connected. These biotic (people, flora and fauna) and abiotic (buildings, programs and infrastructure) relationships are tangibly represented in the connections between Simon Fraser University, SFU Community Trust, and SFU Childcare Society[1] — all stakeholders and, by extension, the mountain, its lands, critters and related watershed. In a greater sense, SFU and UniverCity are a prolific ecosystem in their own right, comprised of people living, learning and working together as a community that is culturally rich, economically viable and ever-respectful of the environment that it is committed to share. Nature is what it needs to be and so it is — apparently thriving atop Burnaby Mountain.

1   SFU Childcare Society is responsible for facilitating the programming at the Centre and has eleven cohesive programs that offer high-quality childcare services (full and part-time) to over 300 children ages 3 months to 13 years old.

[HO·ME·O·STA·SIS]

Noun

The tendency toward a relatively stable equilibrium between interdependent elements, especially as maintained by physiological processes.

Part I: **LOFTY ASPIRATIONS**

"We share a similarity with other developers in that we are focused on generating a profit. We just happen to channel the revenue to create endowment wealth that supports teaching and research."

GORDON HARRIS
President and CEO, SFU Community Trust

DECONSTRUCTING BARRIERS — BUILDING OPPORTUNITIES

There is abundant evidence that SFU Community Trust has worked systematically to develop UniverCity, earning an international reputation for leadership as an environmentally-responsible developer of a world-class sustainable community.

However, it was not easy or automatic as innovative designers and developers alike share a somewhat universal experience of frustration when new ideas and green solutions butt up against outmoded or generalized building codes. The Trust addressed regulations directly with authorities, working together toward a more stringent and sustainable way of doing things on Burnaby Mountain. This progressive, precedent-setting work with the local planning authorities has been vital to the successful implementation of a revolutionary green zoning bylaw that requires all new buildings at UniverCity to be constructed to be at least 35 percent more energy efficient and 45 percent more water efficient than comparable traditional buildings adhering to the City of Burnaby's Building Code. The 35 to 45 percent range is determined on a sliding scale and factors in the relative density of an individual project. Meant to work in concert with the innovative

ordinance-based programs governing SFU lands, the Trust has strategically developed UniverCity's contemporary infrastructure by preparing zoned, serviced, subdivided sites and offering opportunities to "qualified" private sector developers on a prepaid, 99-year leasehold basis. An infrastructure development such as the addition of an ultra-green neighborhood energy utility to serve mountaintop dwellers is a significant example of the facilitative nature, foresight and deep commitment of the Trust. In addition to ambitious (yet achievable) energy-efficiency values, all projects are expected to meet or exceed a set of progressive performance-based requirements such as managing all of the rainwater that falls on the site, specifying predetermined quantities of local materials, and adhering to toxicity requirements for said materials. Traditional barriers were reengineered to foster sustainable planning and design.

18

Neighborhood developments at UniverCity are located within a short walking distance to the Childcare Centre, SFU, public transit and to the shops and services on University High Street.

"How we do things is what matters... We're purposeful and meaningful."

GORDON HARRIS
President and CEO,
SFU Community Trust

19

> *"Pure economic sense dictates that we (the Trust) need to be profitable, distributing money to the endowment fund but it also has to be economically sound for the developers. And it's working — most all of the developers have returned for their second or third site which is proof that the partnerships are successful."*

DALE MIKKELSEN
Director of Development, SFU Community Trust

DEVELOPING SUSTAINABLY

The Trust may appear principally similar to most other developers; however, their sweeping commitment to sustainability is what has set them apart. UniverCity (and its development partners and projects) have received a myriad of awards[2] of excellence that recognize achievements for exemplary planning and development, best practices, innovation, conservation and energy efficiency. And while the community is still less than mid-way through its development progression, local, regional and global recognition has come at each step by well-implemented step. A case in point: in 2008 the American Planning Association awarded its inaugural Planning Excellence Award for "Innovation in Green Community Planning" to the Trust for UniverCity, among a sea of remarkable American projects. Future ecological, social and architectural accolades are virtually assured due to its measured, thoughtful planning approach — inclusive of what is best for the university, the development community and the citizens — that have defined UniverCity.

2   See Appendix: Awards and Recognition

A SUSTAINABLE COMMUNITY APPROACH

Using the OCP as a guide, the Trust mapped a carefully gauged, phased-based program for building out UniverCity, concentrating development within specific neighborhoods. Strategic implementation of high-density projects allowed for proficient infrastructure delivery, incremental growth in sustainability measures, while becoming both greener and more economical than conventional suburban-tract developments. *East Highlands* was UniverCity's first neighborhood and features eight contemporary, sustainably-designed housing developments plus University Highlands Elementary School — all built in accordance with the rigorous environmental standards set by the Trust.

Conveniently located at the eastern end of the SFU's campus, with associated transit services and recreational amenities, *East Highlands* is directly linked to University High Street. The village-style boulevard is comprised of about thirty local stores and services including a full-service grocery, cafes, a financial institution, a travel agency, a range of restaurants, an organic delicatessen, a hair salon, and a pharmacy. The commercial core, brimming with activity, is the heart of the community and is anchored by the Cornerstone and the Hub buildings. Contributing to the mix, additional residences and offices are located above the street-oriented commercial space and draw yet more people and businesses to the urban core. UniverCity's Town Square is located opposite the urban stretch of stores and shops. The public hardscape is designed to serve as a venue for hosting community gatherings and events such as concerts and festivals and is a literal and figurative link to the university. The civic space is flanked by UniverCity's burgeoning *West Highlands* neighborhood.

UniverCity's *West Highlands*, and *South Slopes* neighborhoods are at various stages of development. Discussions for planning of the *fifth and final neighborhood* are evolving and early designs envision a dynamic complement of university and residential uses, including possibilities for additional institutional buildings, community parks and various other community amenities — all impeccably integrated within the existing ecology, community and campus. Every aspect of the infrastructure and the details of every project of UniverCity are thoughtfully planned with the future in mind. The sustainable design jewel of the community, country and beyond is the auspicious UniverCity Childcare Centre Living Building.

22

Parcel 17

Altitude
(Parcel 16)

Parcel 18

Altaire
(Parcels 7 & 8)

Parcel 19

Parcel 20

Water Tower
Building

Novo Two
(Parcel 6)

PHASE 3

Highland
House
(Parcel 23)

UniverCity
Childcare
(Parcel 22)

Richard
Bolton
Park

Aurora
(Parcel 5)

Parcel 21

Verdant
(Parcel 11)

Serenity
(Parcel 10)

Parcel 24

PHASE 2

Parcel 25

University Highlands
Elementary School

Novo
(Parcel 4)

PHASE 1

The Cornerstone
(Parcel 14)

The Hub
(Parcel 15)

Harmony
(Parcel 9)

Origin
(Parcel 27)

Nest
(Parcel 28)

One University
Crescent
(Parcels 2 & 3)

Lift
(Parcel 29)

Parcel 30

Parcel 31

Parcel 32

Parcel 37

Parcel 33

Parcel 34

Parcel 35

Parcel 36

PHASE 4

ENVISIONING THE VERY BEST FOR CHILDREN

Through the 1990s forward, the population of SFU was rising and along with it was an increasing demand for additional childcare capacity to complement existing programs already overseen by the SFU Childcare Society. In 2004, preliminary plans of addressing the growing capacity issues through the expansion of childcare services began to unfold.

Pre-established density requirements for UniverCity led planners to explore scenarios where any potential new facility would be incorporated into a mixed-use development. In 2005, this initiative led to the development of the Verdant Early Childhood Education Centre (children aged 1-3) integrated within the Verdant townhome project, a cluster of sixty LEED Gold homes sold to staff and faculty at a discount of 20 percent below market rates.

In 2006, the Trust considered integrating a second childcare facility for children aged 3-5 into a parkade redevelopment project adjacent to the University High Street core. Initial design plans placed the facility on the rooftop of the parking structure with the intention that it be constructed to a minimum LEED Silver certification level. While the SFU Childcare Society and others were eager for the opportunity to expand

"I was very happy when Gordon Harris came along and created a whole different relationship with the Childcare Society. When we began to talk about a childcare centre that would be on the ground, it was a huge victory for children."

PATRICIA FROUWS
Executive Director, SFU Childcare Society

services within UniverCity, some stakeholders were not at all excited by the prospect of the facility being directly associated with a parking garage. Committed through its mission and actions *"To provide the highest quality of childcare services to children..."* the university's Childcare Society viewed this route as a compromise that they were reluctant to accept. Their objection was based on the belief that children should be valued, deserving of a place to develop their potential through freedom to explore and engage the world around them that included a building with its own footprint — "on the ground" — with high-quality outdoor space conducive to enriched exploration, play and learning.

The SFU Childcare Society and the SFU Faculty of Education were yearning for a facility beyond the normative uninspired social paradigms that did not marginalize childcare, but rather elevated the care and development of children to that of a child-focused community. Not only was the Trust listening intently — they recognized the inherent value and future significance of the opportunity and soon the Trust team was on side, spiritedly championing a brighter, bolder vision for a dedicated childcare centre at UniverCity.

Valuing the expertise and foresight of the SFU Childcare Society, the Trust negotiated with the municipality for an alternative

solution for the facility and abandoned the notion of the parkade project, given a decline in parking requirements at the university due to the success of transit ridership. A detailed transit and commuter ridership model was produced that demonstrated to SFU and the City of Burnaby that there was no longer a need for a 1500-space parking complex. Supportive of a new, much better model, the City of Burnaby agreed that the residential density requirements currently assigned to a development site adjacent to the community park and elementary school could be reallocated to a neighboring site, effectively maintaining the integrity of the OCP and the development density. In exchange for nixing the parkade plan, the Trust was able to make a significant contribution to the endowment fund and was freed of any obligation to build additional parking. Not only was no value lost, the transaction proved to be a defining moment leading toward a superlative solution for the children and their families, UniverCity and SFU.

In 2008, in consultation with the SFU Childcare Society and SFU's Faculty of Early Childhood Education (ECE), the Trust made the bold decision to move the facility. The site was perfectly suited for making history, a Living Building by the name of UniverCity Childcare Centre.

THE GREENEST CHILDCARE CENTRE IN THE WORLD IS HERE

Location, location, location. Immediately adjacent to the university campus, the UniverCity Childcare Centre is located in the heart of UniverCity. The Centre is situated slightly uphill, only a few hundred meters from the urban center sweet spot — a vibrant main thoroughfare, aptly named University High Street. Conveniently located next door is the University Highland Elementary School; a LEED Gold retrofit of an under-utilized campus building that now hosts nearly two hundred students, resulting out of a partnership between the Burnaby School District, the Trust, the City of Burnaby, and SFU. A variety of residential apartments, condominiums and townhomes are located a short walk away from the schools, shops and recreational facilities that make up UniverCity. The prime location of the Centre relates directly to the importance of the Childcare Centre in this intentional community that values people and planet equally.

The varying landscape elevations invite children to climb up and jump down. Weaving paths, ramps, stone steps and an impressive giant silver slide connect all of the different attractions and lookout points while inviting the children to freely explore the Centre's grounds and playful art forms.

27

GREEN EDUCATED

Aside from the telltale signage above the tall front entrance, the exterior of the Childcare Centre gives little away as to the primary function of the building or to its many clever, self-sustaining attributes.

Built into the graded slope of Burnaby Mountain and backed by a lofty evergreen coniferous forest, the most promising sightlines to the building lay mainly to-and-from the south, gradually angling to the treed skyline from University High Street and the community square. The educational and recreational features most likely to provide the best cues to the building typology remain tactfully concealed — shielded out of sight — inside, and on the opposite flank of the building. Sharp architectural lines and a simple mix of carefully selected materials complemented by a boreal forest-inspired palette of colors combine for a modern, yet natural appearance that fits perfectly into the mountain-top setting of the new urban village. While stylish and attractive, the building expresses a mature aesthetic indicative of elegant west coast design. Rather then relying on architectural devices or faux features that request attention, its impressive yet unassuming presence blends seamlessly within the urban-natural setting.

While the exterior of the structure may only provide subtle hints as to the use of the building and the nature of its occupants, the UniverCity Childcare Centre experience begins the moment one sets foot inside the front entrance of the building. Thanks to floor-to-ceiling glazing, the voluminous double-height foyer (and the entire common area) is generously day-lit, facilitating a pleasant transition from the outside-in. Upon entering the foyer and viewing the diminutive furnishings (adorned with playful artwork, coat hooks with colorful garments, nametags, and cubbies stuffed with little bags and boots), most questions are answered about the identity of the inhabitants. Depending on the time of day one arrives at the Centre, visitors are bound to experience firsthand an abundance of 3 to 5 year-old children excitedly milling in and around the airy, cheerful building. The sound of youngsters playing (hence learning) is prevalent except perhaps at naptime, and the daily rhythm of parents and relatives dropping off or collecting their children adds to the lively community whirr of the Centre.

"Dale said to me 'We've got an opportunity here — this could be a Living Building...' and he convinced me immediately. We took it to the Board and they said that we could do whatever we wanted as long as it was within the set budget — and we proceeded to build the greenest childcare facility on the planet."

GORDON HARRIS
President and CEO, SFU Community Trust

BRINGING THE LIVING BUILDING CHALLENGE TO UNIVERCITY

The Cascadia Green Building Council is the Pacific Northwest chapter of the United States Green Building Council (USGBC) and the Canada Green Building Council (CaGBC), and now it is a part of the International Living Future Institute. The SFU Community Trust has been an active member of Cascadia Green Building Council since 2005. The Trust has supported the organization's original green building driver known as Leadership in Energy and Environmental Design (LEED), a third-party certification program, and has implemented numerous projects at UniverCity including Canada's first LEED certified elementary school, a LEED Silver mixed-use building featuring a 23,000 square foot market and over 140 apartment homes, and a LEED Gold affordable housing project. Dale Mikkelsen recognized that the missions of the Cascadia Green Building Council and SFU Community Trust were closely aligned — both valuing the sustainable development of communities, sites and buildings that are to be *socially just, culturally rich and ecologically restorative* and joined Cascadia, eventually bringing his leadership to the organization's Board of Directors.

Mikkelsen was actively connected to the organization's green building advocacy initiatives and was well informed about the Imperatives of the Living Building Challenge — a revolutionary green building certification program that defines the most advanced measure of sustainability in the built environment possible today. He recognized that projects that achieve this level of performance can claim to be the "greenest" anywhere, and would serve as exemplary models for others that follow. The fact that the Living Building Challenge was performance-based rather than a prescriptive model fit well with the Trust's overall design philosophy for the development. The Trust and the various stakeholders had a powerful notion that if they were going to put people in the most sustainable building that can be built, and that children were most deserving of the opportunity so that they may grow up with a new paradigm of expectations for the places they inhabit, then a Living Building was the only option. There was a pervading sense among those involved that this was the right time and ideal place to "pay it forward" and committed to the construction of the UniverCity Childcare Centre as a Living Building.

Trust staff proceeded to present the project (and their ambitious plans to pursue the Living Building Challenge) to their Board of Directors for endorsement. Prudently, the Board approved, but with the proviso that the construction budget remain fixed at the pre-established amount that was allocated for the original project targeted for LEED Silver certification level.

UniverCity Childcare

WORLD-CLASS BUILDING — WORLD-CLASS EDUCATION — WORLD-CLASS SETTING

Opportunity was knocking and fate was replying. Not only were engaged parties advocating for a beautiful, inspiring and functional space befitting the very best care for 3 to 5 year-old children, educators were thinking beyond the physical attributes of a high-performance, ecological-designed facility to the implementation of an innovative educational philosophy, every bit as remarkable and visionary as the building itself.

Regarded to be one of the world's finest preschool curriculum programs, and a perfect fit for the UniverCity Childcare Centre Living Building, the Reggio Emilia[3] philosophy emphasizes three "teachers" — the educator,

3 Reggio Emilia is a town located in northern Italy. Derived from its place of origin, the Reggio Approach to preschool education was started by Reggio Emilia schools following World War II. This methodology has become increasingly well-known all over the world and is considered to be an extraordinary methodology for early childhood education.

the environment, and the community. The Reggio approach follows a teacher-inquiry methodology where educators explore an emergent curriculum and project-based learning related to the Reggio Emilia-inspired philosophy. The intersection of an exceptional educational philosophy was intersecting with noble green design values. The striking alignment between Canada's most sustainable community, a childcare centre built to the world's greenest building standard, and a passionate group of designers, educators and citizens was coalescing.

"Simon Fraser University
is justifiably proud of
its role in helping to
create the greenest
childcare on the planet."

ANDREW PETTER
President and
Vice-Chancellor,
Simon Fraser University

"It matters hugely to us
that the project succeeded.
We put a great deal of
pressure on Fraser Health,
the City of Burnaby and
everybody involved to
work to get the project
completed in a timely
way because the project
was so important."

GORDON HARRIS
President and CEO,
SFU Community Trust

33

THE LIVING BUILDING CHALLENGE™

Simon Fraser University accepted version 1.3 of the Living Building Challenge in 2008. Authored and conceived by Jason F. McLennan, the Living Building Challenge has been issued by the International Living Future Institute, inviting all building owners, architects, design professionals, engineers and contractors to build in a way that provides for a sustainable future. Living Building Challenge 1.3 contained sixteen "Imperatives" categorized within six performance areas known as "Petals". Qualifying projects fell into one of four types: renovation, landscape or infrastructure, building, or neighborhood. The Living Building Challenge has since refined through several iterations (LBC 2.1 has eight Petals and twenty Imperatives). However, the principal philosophy and fundamental tenets of the standard have essentially remained unchanged. Below is a brief summary of the Challenge. Full text of the Living Building Challenge 1.3 is archived with the ILFI. Digital copies of the most current version of the program are available through the International Living Future Institute website: **living-future.org/lbc/about**.

EMBRACING THE CHALLENGE

The Living Building Challenge™ is the built environment's most rigorous performance standard. It calls for the creation of building projects at all scales that operate as cleanly, beautifully and efficiently as nature's architecture. To be certified under the Challenge, projects must meet a series of ambitious performance requirements, including net zero energy, waste and water. Then, once operational and occupied, provide performance data drawn over a full year.

SITE PETAL

Restoring a healthy coexistence with nature

Imperative 1 Responsible Site Selection
Imperative 2 Limits to Growth
Imperative 3 Habitat Exchange

WATER PETAL

Creating water-independent sites, buildings and communities

Imperative 10 Net Zero Water
Imperative 11 Sustainable Water Discharge

ENERGY PETAL

Relying only on current solar income

Imperative 4 Net Zero Energy

INDOOR QUALITY PETAL

Maximizing physical and psychological health and well-being

Imperative 12 Civilized Environment
Imperative 13 Healthy Air: Source Control
Imperative 14 Healthy Air: Ventilation

MATERIALS PETAL

Endorsing products and processes that are safe for all species through time

Imperative 5 Red List
Imperative 6 Construction Carbon Footprint
Imperative 7 Responsible Industry
Imperative 8 Appropriate Materials/ Services Radius
Imperative 9 Leadership in Construction Waste

BEAUTY AND INSPIRATION PETAL

Celebrating design that creates transformative change

Imperative 15 Beauty and Spirit
Imperative 16 Inspiration and Education

35

PART II

Doing Right by Children

The Team, the Process and the Approach

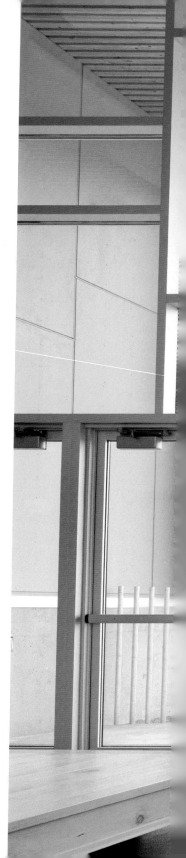

EXIT →

37

"We have such a brief opportunity to pass on to our children our love of this Earth, and to tell our stories. These are the moments when the world is made whole. In my children's memories, the adventures we've had together in nature will always exist."

RICHARD LOUV
Last Child in the Woods

TAKING ON THE CHALLENGE

Reconciling the built environment with the natural environment to create a sustainable future is an exceedingly tall order.

The UniverCity Childcare Centre was one of the first projects in the world to sign up for the Living Building Challenge and one of only a handful of initiatives in North America at the time to officially commit to the built environment's most rigorous performance standard. A trio of British Columbia projects registered for the Challenge in 2008-2009, indicative of the bold green-design leadership emerging out of Canada's western-most province.

Several other groundbreaking projects located just south in Seattle, Washington, also inspired by the Challenge's visionary call, made for a distinct concentration of Living Building initiatives in the Pacific Northwest. The International Living Future Institute's ambitious and thought-provoking call to action had a palpable presence in the Cascadia region. The Challenge had established an undeniable foothold in the Pacific Northwest as evidenced by these initiatives and, of special note, a Living Building for young children like no other, located on the summit of Burnaby Mountain.

Advocates of the new UniverCity Childcare Centre envisioned the facility to be the first of

its kind in Canada and the greenest childcare facility in the world. Aspirations and accolades not withstanding, the Trust viewed the completion of the Centre as a salient marker of ecological design progress — the creation of a prototype of what could be achieved and replicated elsewhere. The fact that the accomplishment would benefit generations to come solidified their resolve to see the Centre through as nothing less than a Living Building.

For the new UniverCity Childcare Centre to become a bona fide Living Building, a coalition of talented and determined individuals who valued the broader vision of the SFU Community Trust would be required. And to be certified under the Challenge, the Centre would have to meet a series of demanding performance requirements, including net zero energy, waste and water, quantified over a minimum of twelve months of continuous occupancy. Following a full year of operations (and the collection of requisite performance data), buildings are eligible for an independent third-party audit to determine whether or not the project has met some, or all of the Imperatives of the Challenge. Then, and only then, could the Centre obtain full Living Building status with the ILFI.

UniverCity Childcare

39

> *"UniverCity is unique, and we work continuously to make sure that the best of what we do here can be replicated — easily and affordably — elsewhere."*

DALE MIKKELSEN
Director of Development,
SFU Community Trust

FIRST ASCENT

Gordon Harris and Dale Mikkelsen considered the Trust fortunate to work with a number of groups that supported their vision.

Following the momentous decision to build a dedicated childcare centre to the most rigorous green building standard in the world, Trust staff lost no time issuing a Request For Proposals (RFP) to a half-dozen select firms, prospecting for a design team with the appropriate qualifications and the willingness to be on the sharp end of this most-ambitious and unprecedented of projects.

Also known as design-tender, design-bid-build (D-B-B) is purposed to hold a firm to the pre-established budget. Looking for a fixed price at tender and the associated quality and efficiencies that arise from related competition, the Trust specified an RFP that called for the traditional D-B-B method of project delivery. The Trust

planned to retain a locally led architecture firm that would, in turn, work closely with the Trust to identify the design direction of the project. In preparation for the bidding phase, the architect would then produce tender documents to be used to secure various general contractors. The proposition was sound though somewhat complex (later on, numerous issues would need to be resolved regarding jurisdiction of regulatory bodies before the tender could be issued). Acknowledging that D-B-B pricing is difficult before design is fully completed and presuming that there was going to be a learning curve because of the unknowns associated with constructing a Living Building, the Trust forged ahead with measured confidence.

RESOLUTE TO RISE UP

Due to the relative newness of the Living Building Challenge, the roster of designers anywhere in the world with practical experience working on Living Buildings was at best, limited.

Undeterred, Harris and Mikkelsen knew the potential talent pool of local, ambitious designers, literally within sight of Burnaby Mountain, was among the deepest to draw from in North America. The same optimistic driving force of the Trust that had elevated the would-be project from the original parkade rooftop scenario to the daring possibility of becoming a Living Building was fortified by a strong belief that the ideal alliance of people to meet the Challenge was nearby in the renowned green-design epicenter of Vancouver, British Columbia.

From the beginning, Trust staff knew the project required an architecture firm that was versatile, experienced, and able to solve problems with creativity and innovation. Mikkelsen had in mind his top pick of architects who he believed was capable of leading the project from initial conceptual stages to an operational, elegant Living Building. He knew that in order to administer the project effectively, the project required a firm that lived and breathed integrated design and was not timid about venturing into the largely uncharted world of Living Building design — on a fixed budget no less. Rising to the top and recognized as one of the leading design studios in Canada, Vancouver's Hughes Condon Marler Architects (HCMA) had both the outstanding project pedigree and an exceptionally talented cadre of designers. Not only did HCMA have extensive experience working within the constraints of challenging construction budgets, Mikkelsen believed that HCMA had the requisite appetite for

innovation and the far-sighted leadership crucial to successfully meet the lofty tenets of the Living Building Challenge.

HCMA was intrigued. Not only was the project pushing the outer envelope of ecological design, it included the very best in early childhood education in the form of the Reggio Emilia pedagogy. The two pre-eminent philosophies shared powerful synergies, so in sync with each other that the prospect of being involved was exciting. The HCMA proposal eloquently summed up their advanced understanding of what was most important for the UniverCity Childcare Centre to be the very best it could be.

It is critical that this project embody a strong commitment to sustainable design and collaborative processes. We feel that a focus on architectural quality is a key component for the well-being of the children. Their ability to learn and develop will be significantly enhanced from being in an environment designed to be as sustainable as possible; an environment that lives and breathes alongside them. Our ongoing challenge, and inspiration, is to reveal that sustainable design is creative and innovative, and that we can balance environmental sensitivity with exceptional architectural quality.

Further, HCMA inherently valued the principles necessary to shepherd the green design strategies for the UniverCity Childcare Centre. "Social Sustainability", "Economic Sustainability" and "Environmental Sustainability" had evolved to become doctrine at HCMA, woven into the fabric of the firm and imbued in its finest work. Karen Marler, HCMA Partner and principal-in-charge for the Living Building project, possessed a unique understanding that community wellness was closely linked to well-designed and meaningfully located places and she held a deep conviction that architectural quality would play an essential role in realizing the highest potential outcome of the project. The opportunity to design for present and future generations

of children was a powerful draw for Marler and, as it turned out, for everybody on the team with children in their lives. Not only did HCMA's philosophy dovetail neatly with the Trust's vision for the UniverCity Childcare Centre, together they were preparing to elevate ecological design to a whole new level.

Aim Towards Living Building — This framework is redefining green building design. By going beyond LEED Gold, additional commitments from all parties will be required to deliver a Living Building for the UniverCity Childcare Facility. Attempting to do so will be challenging and some of the LB prerequisites might not be applicable for this facility. However, the team will aim at delivering a Living Building to further enhance the multiple sustainable strategies already in place at UniverCity. We propose an Integrated Design Process (IDP) to establish and prioritize the green building goals important to UniverCity. The IDP will be done considering the nature of the project, its context, budget and specific requirements. We believe that UniverCity should tackle all prerequisites of the Living Building Challenge and assess the feasibility at every stage of the design to ensure that educational, social, environmental and economical goals are not compromised in the process.

The original RFP denoted three parameters for the project: 1. That the facility is built to a level of LEED Platinum or Living Building, 2. The facility is designed to the concepts of the Reggio Emilia early childhood education curriculum and 3. The building is mobile so that it could be transported in five or six years to another location around UniverCity. The mobility aspect was eventually dropped. Regardless, HMCA was game for all parameters, and eager for the opportunity to do new, innovative work, setting their sights squarely on designing nothing less than a Living Building.

43

SFU Trust Leadership, Gordon Harris and Dale Mikkelsen with Karen Marler, Principal, HCMA

THE RIGHT TEAM FOR HIGHER CLIMBS

The Trust's recruitment of HCMA proved to be a sharp decision in fortifying the future success of the Centre.

Through years of experience, HCMA had built relationships with a talented lineup of consultants whose work and ideals were akin to those of HCMA. Those connections brought key professional talent with a passion for innovation to the UniverCity Childcare Centre project.

Structural engineering firm Fast + Epp, having proven themselves through exceptional work, brought "hands on" familiarity with Living Buildings and a collaborative spirit to the alliance. Cobalt Engineering (now known as Integral Group) was selected for their advanced mechanical systems design and also possessed substantial knowledge of the Living Building Challenge. Both Fast + Epp and Integral's team had garnered significant

knowledge about Living Building design from their work on the Vancouver Parks Board's Van Dusen Gardens Visitor Centre, which was valuable despite being a project with a very different design and building typology. Electrical engineering firm MMM, known for its professional acumen, innovation and willingness to collaborate for best solutions, rounded out the core consultant team. Notably, ECOfluid Systems, a Canadian cleantech company specializing in the design and construction of wastewater treatment installations, worked very closely with the core team in exploring highly innovative solutions for treating blackwater at the Centre.

INTEGRATED
DESIGN DEFINED

Over-simplified, the rationale supporting integrated design may be distilled down to the adage "two heads are better than one."

A holistic philosophy that recognizes the intricacies of architecture and engineering are best addressed through a dynamic collaboration of experts with a stake in the project, which leads to creative solutions and best possible outcomes. The Trust and HCMA were both advocates of, and well-practiced in, the venerated and artful application of integrated design. For the Centre project they were eager to leverage the professional resolve of diverse disciplines, and to reach out well beyond the design table in search of creative ideas. Emboldened by the apparent breadth and depth of the design team and their inclusive plans, the Trust was ready to forge ahead.

"Like any initiative that is endeavoring to change a culture, the ultimate success of the Living Building Challenge will be part revolution, part evolution."

KAREN MARLER
Principal, HCMA

45

CREATIVE, NATURE-BASED SPACE

Known for its simple approach and organic, contemporary recreation concepts, the homegrown landscape design firm space2place was selected for its expertise well beyond industry norms for designing innovative children's play environments.

Principal Alison Maddaugh had worked closely with Susan Harrington, a Professor of Architecture and Landscape Architecture at the University of British Columbia, who had published the highly acclaimed report titled *7 Cs: An Informational Guide to Young Children's Outdoor Play Spaces* (see Sidebar). Serving as special advisor to the consultant team, Harrington's research and Vancouver-based report for early childhood educators, designers and parents alike, provided insightful guideposts that informed the innovative approach of space2place and HCMA. The seminal report was perfectly suited to addressing the principles of the Reggio Emilia pedagogy. Many of these "Cs" such as *connectivity, context, change and chance*, fulfilled Reggio Emilia's emphasis on "the environment as a third teacher" and fell perfectly in step with the health, beauty and materials canons emphasized by the Challenge.

The Trust's inherent confidence in HCMA to lead, effectively triggered the assembly of a core team that was open to operating outside customary comfort zones, and had a proclivity to engage in the collaborative process crucial to addressing the complexities of Living Building design. Running against the progressive backdrop of UniverCity, the team relished the opportunity to be key players in a project evidenced to be as challenging as extraordinary.

A Vancouver-based study identified Seven Cs that should be considered when designing outdoor play spaces for young children.

7 Cs: An Informational Guide to Young Children's Outdoor Play Spaces, Susan Harrington with Chandra Lesmeister, Jamie Nicholls, and Kate Stefiuk, 2007, *Vancouver: Westcoast Childcare Resource Centre*

7 Cs

CHARACTER: Refers to the overall feel and design intent of your outdoor play space. Light quality is balanced, overall softness of materials are considered, and there are color differentials.

CONTEXT: Refers to the small world of the play space itself, the larger world that surrounds the centre, and how they interact with each other. Micro-climatic conditions are addressed. Views are provided to the outside world or secured against if dangerous.

CONNECTIVITY: Indicates the physical, visual, and cognitive connectedness of the play space itself. A hierarchy of pathways, both indoor and outdoor are connected visually.

CHANGE: Involves a range of differently sized spaces and how the play space changes over time. There should be spaces to be alone or for two, spaces for large group activity, water, mud, pea gravel, vegetation, and a large sand area for four or more children.

CHANCE: Involves an occasion that allows something to be done; an opportunity for the child to create, manipulate, and leave an impression on the play space. The area should be set up for loose parts, messy zones, and mystery.

CLARITY: Combines physical legibility and perceptual imageability. Both visual clarity and sound clarity are significant.

CHALLENGE: Refers to the physical and cognitive encounters that challenge, such as: equipment, platforms, and other structures of varying heights. Other possibilities include: climbing opportunities on ladders, ropes, and nets, flat open space to run or play ball, space to ride a bike quickly, looping circulation for a tricycle, grassy slopes to roll down, tunnels or other apertures to crawl through, stepping stones, log rounds, or balance beam/logs, swings, bars to hang from and slides at a challenging height.

47

INTEGRATED DESIGN ++

There was an intuitive relationship between Living Buildings and the eco-educational philosophy to be implemented at the Centre.

Marler and Mikkelsen considered it critical for everyone to understand what the common goals and objectives were for the Centre and welcomed many cooks into the kitchen. Through a series of workshops and charrettes, HCMA and the Trust brought together a variety of parties including planners from the City of Burnaby, licensing officials from the Fraser Health Authority, the Director and several teachers from the SFU Childcare Society, and the full consultant team.

Invitations were extended beyond mere courtesy. Rather, there was a genuine spirit of collaboration and transparency, intent on valuing the input of everyone — ensuring creativity and innovative solutions for meeting the design, and programmatic goals of the project. Active participation and brainstorming around the concept of "what does a Living Building look like?" and "what is Reggio Emilia?" framed discussions about the project. Early on, facilitators teased out the natural symmetry between the principles of the Challenge and

the philosophy of the emergent, educational approach with the namesake of a town in Northern Italy known as Reggio Emilia.

In one of the initial charrettes, Jason F. McLennan, International Living Future Institute, CEO and visionary behind the Living Building Challenge presented his literal and figurative impressions of what a Living Building can be. Following McLennan's inspirational presentation, early childcare education expert Susan Harrington provided valuable insights into the core characteristics of the Reggio Emilia pedagogy. The two philosophies melded into one conversation as the group recognized a growing number of values-based connections embedded within the models. Complexities notwithstanding, the synergies emerging around the project were powerful. Another series of very special workshops featuring the young, would-be occupants of the Centre proved ultimately inspirational for the design team.

"We knew that if we were to meet this objective that we couldn't plug in anything after, that it had to be a fully-integrated process that included everyone. We took it to that level and included 3 to 5 year olds in the charrette process to make sure we were creating a building that they would actually want to inhabit."

DALE MIKKELSEN
Director of Development,
SFU Community Trust

48

SFU Preschool Children's Workshop "What makes a great play environment?" Children were encouraged to build and discuss their ideal play environment using modelling clay.

"It was valuable to have little, young designers helping out."

JAY LIN
Architect, HCMA

A LIVING BUILDING THROUGH A DIFFERENT LENS

Any project with a design charrette involving preschoolers is extraordinary.

Appreciating that the Living Building Challenge calls for an exceedingly holistic approach, the design team cast their net well beyond the radius of sustainable design norms to include workshops starring 3 to 5 year olds from a neighboring SFU Childcare facility, plus their families, educators and members of the design team. While engaging future occupants of a building was nothing particularly progressive, listening to, and valuing the wishes of preschoolers certainly was. And while it has become increasingly commonplace for design teams to solicit the input of stakeholders, the fledgling insights coming from these all-ages charrettes would shape the Centre in tangible and profound ways. The design team listened intently to what the children desired for their ideal play area and several experiential and imaginative themes were revealed that involved climbing, jumping, and playing with elemental materials such as wood, water and sand.

49

"The Center is the next step in a new millennium of childcare facilities."

PATRICIA FROUWS
Executive Director, SFU Childcare Society

"We are pushing the normative boundaries of modern childcare."

KAREN VAUGHAN
UniverCity Childcare Program Director

I like long slides- this ones long
I like this slide it goes a little curve

CLIMB UP HIGH

Play and discovery is serious work.

The fresh insights of the children and those of the educators astonished HCMA. Shared perceptions of bright, airy, voluminous space, ("climb up high") and play elements such as the magnificent two-storey silver slide, ("I like long slides — this one's long", "I like this slide-it goes a little curve" and "fire breathing dragon!"), are some of the thoughts that informed the design of the Centre's community spaces and complemented the educational programming. It was the happy job of the designers to ponder the inspirations articulated by the children (verbally, and in drawings, sketches, and models) and translate those sometimes whimsical, sometimes physical, ideas into the design.

Karen Marler recognized that some of the most powerful information for the architectural team came from yet another outside source — the care providers. HCMA actively solicited input and SFU Childcare Society leadership eagerly brought forth the elegant concepts of Transparency, Light, and Community. Patricia Frouws asked that the educators who worked with the children be consulted about the practical aspects of the facility. Faced with opportunity to weigh in on an essentially blank slate, purposeful details meshed with holistic design in the common area layout, sightlines to washrooms, play areas, and the configuration of dynamic indoor amenities and organically-inspired outdoor space. The Centre's loft-like mezzanine, double-height community space and expansive glazing are indoor examples where HCMA fastidiously merged the ideas of workshop participants with their own constructs, embedding sound practicalities within the refined design of the Living Building. HCMA heeded the children's intuitive wishes and the educator's hands-on insights, bringing opportunities for delight and discovery to the Centre — folding play and education elegantly into the overall design.

"*I was asked from the very beginning to be involved. I was thrilled by the whole process and even was invited to have a say in selecting the architect.*"

PATRICIA FROUWS
Executive Director,
SFU Childcare Society

51

Part II: **DOING RIGHT BY CHILDREN**

> *"By pursuing the Living Building Challenge™ program, arguably the most advanced green building certification program in the world, the SFU UniverCity Childcare Centre is considered the greenest childcare centre on the planet."*
>
> **JASON F. MCLENNAN**
> CEO, International Living Future Institute

52

PRESENT AND FUTURE

The Centre was shaping up to be a bridge between generations.

And in many ways, Patricia Frouws served as a connector between the Trust, the design team and the various regulatory bodies associated with licensing the Centre. Fellow proponent of Reggio Emilia and longtime colleague, Associate Professor Margaret MacDonald Ph.D. of the SFU Faculty of Education, was also invited to contribute to the design concept from the very beginning, based on her expertise in inter-generational programming and teacher-inquiry methodologies. Her focus areas included the study of innovative early learning curriculums and pedagogical documentation. MacDonald had identified a vital opportunity to conduct early-learning education research on-site as a means to reflect upon and inform best practices. She secured an infrastructure grant through the Canadian Foundation for Innovation (CFI) targeting state-of-the-art research initiatives that are considered to be world class and are deemed to strengthen Canada's standing in a global knowledge economy. The CFI funding, in due course, paid for all the information technology equipment and the eco-furnishings throughout the Centre. Great partnerships between Simon Fraser University, the Faculty of Education, SFU Childcare Society and the Trust flourished, based on the far-sighted recognition that investing in the future of children and education was indeed, a very good idea.

53

"The Childcare Centre is a huge tribute to the childcare field. Historically, we have been marginalized so seeing so many people care about early learning is enormous. Why wouldn't we try and do this for our children?"

MARGARET MACDONALD, Ph.D.
SFU Faculty of Education

DESIGNED FOR EDUCATION — DEDICATED TO CHILDREN

The Centre is a standing example for society to look to in reconsidering priorities for children and the childcare industry.

"Making due" or the repurposing of existing buildings not designed with the care of children in mind, often for temporary daily use, such as church basements and spare rooms, is an unfortunate reality of childcare today. Most facilities offer limited access to quality outdoor play experiences (and associated developmental opportunities) and although they may meet current regulations, facilities are often constructed and furnished extensively with materials now commonly known to be toxic. "Making due" evidently was not part of the master plan at UniverCity.

Dedicated, intentional, healthy spaces are a joy for occupants of all ages. The decision to devote precious square footage to observation and research, and to allocate a portion of the upper mezzanine to educators was significant. Rarely are childcare facilities designed with suitable space for educators to conduct advanced functions such as the documentation of pedagogical narrations and detailed academic enquiries. Not only did the mezzanine and research room, both overlooking the community space, provide ideal vantages, their very existence was emblematic. For educators, it acknowledged that their work was considered formative, important, and respected. For parents it signaled that their children's care and development was of utmost importance at the Centre.

Speaking to the potential long-term education and social implications for children, MacDonald notes, "The message is really loud and clear; you can, and should, deliver the very best for children, affordably. By aiming for the most rigorous building design standard and incorporating an exemplary eco-educational, early-childhood educational philosophy, the Centre has blown away minimum standards for the childcare industry, redefining what is possible for children." Harris, Mikkelsen, Marler and others who have been deeply involved in the creation of the UniverCity Childcare Centre, all emphatically state that "it (the Centre) is the right thing to do."

54

> *"Dedicated space is considered instrumental in bringing education alive. The importance of 'dedicated space' for childcare-based education at the Centre was identified from an early conceptual stage, and is now in practice (and play) today."*

DALE MIKKELSEN
Director of Development, SFU Community Trust

TRANSPARENCY, LIGHT AND COMMUNITY

Symmetry, balance, and verve.

The concepts of *Transparency, Light, and Community* sought by SFU Childcare Society educators were already deep-seated in the design DNA of architects at Hughes Condon Marler. The acquiescence of educational and creative principles was advancing design of the Centre in constructs relating to transparency, light and community (See Indoor Quality Petal and Beauty and Inspiration Petal). It was important for all concerned that perceptible barriers to moving from inside to outside be minimized. Flowing access, physically and visually, to the experiences, emotions and feelings associated with the Centre's dynamic outdoor environment is facilitated by the expansive glazing throughout the building and well-located egresses.

56

A constructed, functional fluvial rill, shaped in a Fibonacci-like arc around a landscaped slope and the Centre's sandpit, channels rainwater from the rooftop alongside a pathway down to an infiltration gallery.

"The power of the UniverCity Childcare is that each child who spends their days there will be touched by the principles that the building demonstrates. Hopefully, they carry the lessons it teaches with them throughout their lives."

AMANDA STURGEON
Vice President, ILFI

"When the sun is out you know it, when it's raining or snowing you can witness it from a protected environment. The transparency of the building allows children to be connected to nature."

JAY LIN
Architect, HCMA

BLURRING THE BOUNDARIES

The design of the Centre supports human relationships and community connections.

"For the team 'integrated design' did not just mean all the design practitioners sitting at the table. They opted to take it to the next level by incorporating the children, the early childhood care provider and the university researchers."

DALE MIKKELSEN
Director of Development,
SFU Community Trust

Unobstructed sightlines from community spaces to the playground and also beyond the facility to a forested neighboring public park, elementary school, residences and commercial buildings, allow children and adults alike to be connected, and make real-time connections to the world going on around the Centre. Children who may be engaged in visual arts inside are free to respond fluidly to changing weather conditions, social dynamics and activities at the Centre's numerous playground focal points. Whether a child chooses to interact with others or opts for a quiet respite from busy Centre life, the openness of the building design supports the educational programming, as well as the social and developmental requisites of the children.

The proclivity of the children to move to and fro from social scenarios to occasional, solo introspective moments goes a long way in accommodating the shifting needs, creativity and curiosity of individuals within the Centre's community. Children themselves regulate the rhythm and nature of their own learning, moving and acting more freely than in traditional childcare scenarios. The perceived (and actual) liberation of the children to move easily from the interior to the outside to experience the dynamic, changing environment is unique. Learning opportunities that come from naturally occurring experiences like snowfall, rain showers and the warmth of sunlight are suitably complemented by the compelling draw of a myriad of opportunities for play.

Placed thoughtfully around the grounds are numerous elements designed to facilitate a variety of playful experiences. Notably, there are zones purposed for *active, social, creative, nature and fantasy-oriented* experiences. Delineations between these elements are invisible — overlapping and changing endlessly with the perception and imagination of each child. At any particular moment, the three cedar huts (also known to the children as "stick houses", "Three Little Pigs houses", forts) are a fanciful traditional village. The tree stump climber may be an island, the promise of buried treasure in the sand ("sand pit", "sand pool") or the watery power of nature sluicing down the rainwater channel that skirts the ramp may be imagined as a mighty river. As nature provides, water streams off the roof, down the rain chain — a tactile, auditory and visual display. The UniverCity Childcare Centre is the first childcare centre ever to integrate the most-advanced environmental design with the apt tenet of the Reggio Emilia curriculum revering "the environment as the third teacher." Designers saw to it that natural materials were abundant throughout the building and grounds, and that natural opportunities to learn were possible everywhere.

59

OVERCOMING THE GREEN BUILDING PREMIUM

The dream of building the Centre did not materialize without considerable determination in the face of convention.

The ominous preconception looming over the industry, the "green building premium" refers to the presumed additional costs associated with planning, designing and constructing high-performance green buildings. And while an ever-growing number of people now acknowledge the merits of creating buildings that use less energy and water and are constructed with healthy materials, there is still a belief that green building comes with the caveat of substantial additional costs.

To date, the majority of completed *leading-edge* green projects have been done so by organizations that are striving to set a remarkable environmental precedent through their actions and have been prepared to pay a significant premium for their altruism. In many situations, high-quality sustainable design

construction has cost more than traditional construction because the prevailing strategy for greening-up buildings was to upgrade features such as specialized materials, sophisticated HVAC systems and excessive tech bling. While technology-based strategies for sustainable design have been celebrated and touted as innovative, requisite equipment can be expensive, lending to the existing preconception of a significant green premium. A further general lack of understanding about the valuation of upfront capital costs of high-quality buildings versus non-green counterparts is also a significant factor. However, more information is coming to light about the forthcoming economic savings available to green buildings, notably in the form of lower operating and maintenance costs, higher occupancy rates and reduced employee absenteeism to name a few.

60

UniverCity Childcare

EYE TO THE FUTURE — FIRM GRASP OF THE BOTTOM LINE

The traditional approach of weighing upfront costs only has exacerbated the perception of a "green building premium" — at least so far.

Keenly aware of industry advancements and evolving trends toward well-designed, highly-integrated solutions, combined with ample green building knowledge gleaned from their own experience in developing numerous green buildings that comprise UniverCity, the Trust believed early on that they could deliver a remarkable building, even a Living Building, at a cost comparable to traditional market rates. Furthermore, Harris and Mikkelsen understood the significance of such an achievement and were up to the challenge of setting yet another precedent with their work. This time they had their sights set on running said green building premium out of UniverCity for good, and that doing so would have importance far beyond the green reaches of Burnaby Mountain.

"Children are going to be there 8 to 10 hours per day. The building could be the greenest building in the world but if it's not an incredible experience for the children, if it doesn't bring joy, it wouldn't be a success."

DALE MIKKELSEN
Director of Development,
SFU Community Trust

61

BUILDING THE VERY BEST WITH LESS, FOR LESS

The UniverCity Childcare Centre has effectively demonstrated that a Living Building can be built for less than a conventional alternative.

During the development of the Centre, the Trust was tracking other publicly-developed childcare facilities of similar size and form in the region. Many municipalities in and around Vancouver were trending towards the development of childcare facilities in new communities with integrated developer-cost contributions. As a result, construction costs and construction tenders became public data thus providing a ready source of cost comparison. Several projects were cross-referenced, and on average, the UniverCity Childcare facility, as a full turn-key project, was delivered for between 15 and 20 percent lower than comparable projects, most of which were constructed to some level of LEED performance but not necessarily certified.

The pervasive question of "Why go to such great lengths to create buildings to the highest levels of sustainability?" is now being answered by a rising number of third-party advocates of the Centre such as the CaGBC, USGBC and the ILFI, who are enthused by the project's quality and economic success and give the resounding retort of "Why not?" After all, not only is the building design remarkable for addressing the stringent Imperatives of the Challenge, the project's economics are flipping the conventional preconception about green building premiums on its head.

"Whenever you're facing a barrier that's actually been given its own name ('Green Premium'), you have to know that you're up against a resilient roadblock.

DALE MIKKELSEN
Director of Development,
SFU Community Trust

INTENTS OF THE CHALLENGE — BELAYING THE MARKET

At a time when the benefits of designing sustainably are more or less ringing true with everyone, proponents of the Living Building Challenge are fervently pushing beyond current conventions to evoke meaningful, lasting change.

"The UniverCity Childcare Centre is evidence of just how far the green building industry in Canada has come over the last ten years. Not too long ago, designing a LEED Silver building was seen as difficult and costly. Fast forward to 2013, a Living Building has been built below market rates — a significant accomplishment which shows that major advancements in sustainable design need not cost more. This bodes well for next generation buildings in Canada."

THOMAS MUELLER
President & CEO, Canada
Green Building Council

Remarks from Marler and Mikkelsen (plus just about everyone else who has been somehow involved with Living Building projects) are strikingly similar; that the Challenge, its Imperatives and Red List are changing the way they do things... pushing them outside their comfort zone toward nobler design solutions. The positive influence of the Challenge goes way beyond property lines or owners, operators, developers, and design teams. Its Imperatives are radiating outward through supply chains, governmental bodies and decision makers of all kinds wherever they may be.

Construction contractors, regulatory bodies, suppliers, and manufacturers — literally all parties that have a thread of connection to Living Building projects are being challenged to closer examine their processes and principles. The immediate benefactors of the transformation toward "a future that is socially just, culturally rich and ecologically restorative" are the building occupants and everything connected to them.

The proverbial raising of the bar spurred on by the Challenge has impacted the UniverCity Childcare Centre and the larger community. Innovations in critical areas of design (referred to in the Living Building Challenge 1.3 as Petals) such as Site, Energy, Materials, Water, Indoor Quality and Beauty and Inspiration (see Part III) are coalescing into magnificent outcomes. According to the ILFI, the particular methodology utilized to meet the expectations of the Living Building Challenge is relegated to the genius of the design team, which is expected to make informed decisions appropriate to the project and bioregion. Within the novel context of the Challenge, and considering the uniqueness of the Centre (typology, programming and community) with its spectacular, yet challenging bioregion, The Trust, HCMA and the consultant team were approaching unfamiliar ground.

63

*"The Living Building Challenge was new to us.
It was a learning curve in many respects that
we invested ourselves in."*

KAREN MARLER
Principal, HCMA

CHECKING IN WITH THE INTERNATIONAL LIVING FUTURE INSTITUTE

A world with Living Buildings and Communities is new territory.

The ILFI issued the Living Building Challenge to all design professionals, contractors and building owners (to create), to politicians and government officials (to remove barriers), and to all of humanity to reconcile the built environment with the natural environment, into a civilization that fosters greater biodiversity, resilience, and opportunities for life with each adaptation and development. A soaring intent but thanks to the resolve of the Trust, HCMA and a collective of supporters, the Living Building Challenge's ensign was flying high on the summit of Burnaby Mountain.

Not only was the UniverCity Childcare project demonstrating a pioneering commitment to the principles of the Living Building Challenge, it was doing so at a point in time where aspects of the Challenge were relatively new and untested. And while the Centre was one of several Vancouver-region buildings that were simultaneously engaged in the Living Building Challenge, no other project shared the same building typology, geography or climate.

The ILFI had learned quickly that interaction between Living Building Challenge staff and project teams was vital to ensure that the team is successful, and that their "lessons learned" can inform the development of the program moving forward. The uniqueness of designing for and administrating a Living Building project meant additional challenges not commonly faced on other green projects. The upside of working on a cutting edge project like the Centre was a plethora of opportunities for innovation, advanced design knowledge accrual, and to a related degree, opportunities for the ILFI's Living Building Challenge team to examine in detail the application of the Standard's various Imperatives where hammer meets nail. It is widely accepted by the ILFI and the Living Building Challenge Community at-large that the Standard will continue to adapt and evolve over the ensuing years thanks to the experience and feedback coming from projects such as the UniverCity Childcare Centre.

"It's called a challenge for a reason."

JASON F. MCLENNAN
The Originator of the
Living Building Challenge

After a project is registered, the team can begin organizing and submitting documentation through its account on the ILFI's Project Portal. A project team may then elect to receive additional support at the beginning of, or during its design process by choosing from a menu of Technical Assistance services offered by the Institute. As questions arise, project teams can submit requests for technical clarifications via the Dialogue, or refer to the Institute's array of tools and support options.

The documentation process continues through the construction phase and then the operational phase—twelve consecutive months of operation, during which the project performance data is recorded. Once the operational phase is complete, a project team may submit data for audit. Project teams pursuing full certification or "Living" status may opt to undergo a preliminary audit to receive a conditional assessment of Imperatives whose requirements are less likely to be impacted by the operational phase.

65

THE PLAN
TAKES SHAPE

Altruistic ideas about design and nature felt right to everyone involved with the Centre.

The ILFI's ecology-design, design-ecology metaphor describing the creation of buildings that operate as cleanly, beautifully and efficiently as nature's architecture has become common parlance associated with Living Buildings. However, *"complexities in harmony"* may just be the essence of the Living Building Challenge. The translation for the UniverCity Childcare Centre: a cluster of early-adopters must understand and then navigate various principles, regulations, economic conditions and market forces, departments, committees, materials choices and naysayers, all the while petitioning for something largely yet-to-be known — then somehow interconnect the intricate design details in a final form of a customized arrangement of innovations and solutions.

Behind the blue door: SFU Faculty of Education experts conduct innovative early-learning research onsite through a one-way glass overlooking the community space as a means to inform best practices.

SIMPLE VOLUMES

At 5,700 square feet the Centre is designed to accommodate 50, three-to-five year old children and about ten staff members.

Unlike institutional partitioning often found in traditional settings, the Centre's floor plan has generous "community space" (space in excess of local licensing requirements) for shared uses as well as two separate, intentional spaces ("two centres") so that care providers are free to tailor programming based on demographics and children's interests. By scaling the facility appropriately for the site and for the use, and taking the least complicated approach possible to the design of the structure, HCMA tipped the odds for meeting the Challenge in their favor.

A hallmark of the Centre's interior is the generously daylit, naturally ventilated, common areas. Trickle vents allow for fresh air inflow and expansive windows afford ample natural light minimizing the need for supplementary sources. Utilizing a simple palette of building materials, HCMA architects and structural engineering firm Fast + Epp created a customized interior within a functional, box-like structure. Air and light diffuse easily throughout the building. And, when required, in-floor radiant heating effectively distributes thermal comfort. Functionally designed and right-sized for efficiency, the characteristic beauty of the space is innate. Form meets function in the clean horizontal corduroy lines of locally-sourced dimensional lumber, mostly unfinished, that make up the tall walls. The integrated core and shell are predominantly comprised of natural wood, steel struts and beams, and glass. The office spaces, kitchen amenities, customized child-friendly washrooms, sleep room, research room and community spaces all fit thoughtfully inside the practical, yet artful, framework of the building. All details target reduced consumption and waste — revering water and energy (and occupants) as precious resources.

67

"The design team for the UniverCity Childcare Centre project demonstrated an incredible commitment to addressing all aspects of the Living Building Challenge. And in doing so, their discoveries, achievements and lessons learned are contributing to the advancement of restorative design and a sustainable future."

JASON F. MCLENNAN
CEO, International
Living Future Institute

THE PATH TO THE FUTURE

The Centre's status as a Living Building elevates it to a rarified realm along with the most ecologically designed buildings anywhere in the world, so much so that it will be considered ahead of its time for many years to come. And while summing up the long-term cultural implications of the UniverCity Childcare Centre will not be easy without significant retrospect, the legacy will surely live with the children for which a Living Building has become the new normal. In a future where this advanced level of design (and education) is reflected upon as fundamental, it is reasonable and hopeful that the societal and environmental values imbued in the Centre will be carried forth in the children who attend the Centre, fostering a generation of compassionate human beings with a new eco-conscious paradigm.

On July 21, 2010, the Trust ceremoniously broke ground for the Centre at UniverCity's prime locale known then as Parcel 22, signaling the expeditious beginning of the project. Lifted by the pending significance of the pursuit, the team committed to strive for harmony between the Petals of the Living Building Challenge, and to address the complexities that were certain to arise from the Challenge's Imperatives.

PART III

Sum of the Parts

Realizing the Petals of the
Living Building Challenge

EMBRACING THE LIVING BUILDING CHALLENGE

TWO RULES:

1. All Imperatives assigned to a Typology are mandatory. Some Typologies may require fewer Imperatives because the conditions are either not applicable or may compromise other critical needs. However, teams are encouraged to integrate the optional Imperatives into their projects wherever possible.

Many of the Imperatives have temporary exceptions to acknowledge current market limitations. These exclusions are listed in the footnotes of each section of the Living Building Standard. Temporary exceptions are modified or removed as the market changes. Using the Standard as a fulcrum for change, the International Living Future Institute requires advocacy for the essential improvements to the building industry and related manufacturing at-large.

2. Living Building Challenge certification is based on actual, rather than modeled or anticipated, performance. Projects must be operational for at least twelve consecutive months prior to evaluation.

The following chapters of this book focus on the six individual Petals of the Living Building Challenge™ version 1.3:

1. SITE

2. ENERGY

3. MATERIALS

4. WATER

5. INDOOR QUALITY

6. BEAUTY AND INSPIRATION

73

For full text of the Living Building Challenge, please visit www.living-future.org.

NOTE: *In order for a project to receive full Living Building Challenge certification, it must provide performance data from at least 12 months of full operation after occupancy.*

THE SITE PETAL

Community-centric

SUMMARY OF THE LIVING BUILDING CHALLENGE VERSION 1.3 SITE PETAL

Petal Intent

The intent of the Site Petal is to clearly articulate where it is acceptable for people to build, how to protect and restore a place once it has been developed, and to encourage the creation of communities that are once again based on the pedestrian rather than the automobile.

Petal Imperatives

- Habitat Exchange
- Responsible Site Selection
- Limits to Growth

"*Who was the second person on the moon? Who was Canada's second Prime Minister?? Nobody remembers. We have to be first. Being first mattered because we wanted to provide leadership regionally, nationally and internationally around sustainable community building. We have to be first.*"

GORDON HARRIS
President and CEO, SFU Community Trust

GROUNDED REALITY

Early plans for the UniverCity Childcare Centre included the laudable goals of meeting the Living Building Challenge, adhering to the educational principles of Reggio Emilia, and for the new facility to be portable. The thinking behind creating a movable structure was to create conditions to actively respond over time to the changing urban demographics of the community. Planners reasoned that as existing UniverCity neighborhoods matured and new localities came online, the Centre could be placed where it was needed most.

However, after evaluating the project as a Living Building and investigating portable structures with experts, HCMA soon determined that creating a movable structure that met all of the Trust's environmental goals and landed within the set budget was not likely. The Trust also became acutely aware of the proposed location in the heart of the community as an anchoring influence for all that they were trying to achieve on a community-scale. HCMA's groundwork led them to the conclusion that if the Centre was to become a Living Building it would warrant a permanent location and the Trust concurred. Technical challenges and limitations of movable structures notwithstanding, portability was unnecessary given the near-perfect setting selected for the Centre. The team's collective vision of a Living Building evolved to a facility rooted to place.

PEOPLE-ORIENTED

The location selected by the Trust for the UniverCity Childcare Centre is situated next to a park, close to residential areas, public transit and a wide variety of urban amenities.

The Centre's level, horizontal plane streetfront/parkfront entry provides a civilized, naturally aligned route to the neighboring Highland Elementary School. The park, located close by on the east side of the building, will be enhanced with a public plaza in the future. This plaza will serve as a gathering space for pupils of the Childcare Centre and for families of the UniverCity community. HCMA chose to add substantial glazing to the entry façade to accentuate the access, adding elements of attractiveness and transparency. Ultimately, the design orientation of the Centre put public entry on a public space so that children and adults could conveniently congregate and travel car free to and from the Centre.

PREPARING THE GROUND

Attributable to the accumulation of excavated debris from the construction of the university campus, the Centre's site was relatively flat (for a mountain top) with a 3-metre drop, falling from the north side of the property toward the south boundary. Characterized as a very small site, constrained further by the pre-existing local building code that called for 7-metre setbacks, and on top of that, regional childcare regulations stipulating substantial outdoor space per child, HCMA was faced with some pragmatic spatial challenges. Not only did the team members have to account for the elements of the physical building, they were faced with accommodating stormwater catchment and infiltration, generous recreational space, and an appropriate landscaping narrative — all within the relative confines of the site's small footprint.

Marler and her team envisioned the building to be one story, offer high-quality play spaces and offer a desirable street presence. The need to create adequate capacity for the program on the Centre's small site, and the growing awareness that every square foot would count in maximizing the potential of the site, led HCMA to apply for an easement on setbacks with the City of Burnaby. Officials granted the request that allowed the team a little more space to figure into the design — especially to increase the outdoor play area available for the children. Immediately, HMCA took advantage of the 3-metre elevation differential of the site by placing the building partially within the existing earthen berm. The slope also enabled the back half of the building to be buried, contributing to the thermal mass of the structure.

SITE PLAN

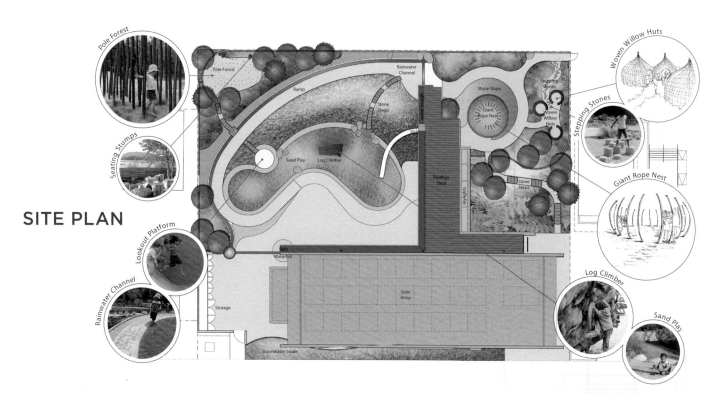

FAR-SIGHTED

HCMA's effective use of the site, supported by the advocacy of the Trust and afforded through the additional wiggle room granted by city planners, allowed HCMA to meet project goals and to reap benefits. Maximizing the available play area was critical for the program and by incorporating the structure partially within the pre-existing berm, a portion of the structure was allowed to become an extension of the children's playspace.

While the orientation of the Centre was largely driven by the need to maximize play areas for the children, the slope of the site and indeed the Centre's southern orientation lent itself to maximizing the potential gains for the solar thermal array. The orientation of the building meant a large exposure for the front façade. HCMA incorporated the conditions into the design by setting back the glazing line and creating a significant overhang that provided useful cover over outdoor play areas. Well-placed louvers were also utilized as effective devices to regulate direct sunlight through the summer months.

Optimizing the attributes of the site was a key aspect for the success of the Centre, both programmatically and for performance while recognizing the simplicity of function desired by the operator.

SITE SUSTAINABILITY

The Living Building Challenge envisions the end of the seemingly never-ending outward growth of development, shifting toward compact, connected communities that conserve natural resources while sustaining human health and that of the native ecosystems.

The progressive development of UniverCity already possessed numerous sustainable qualities inherent to Challenge tenets. The advanced infrastructure of the modern urban community provided near-idyllic conditions for the Centre to leverage solutions for meeting the Site, Energy and Water Petals. By applying a strategy for sharing resources, known within the context of the Challenge as "scale jumping," the Childcare Centre could effectively trade on land, buildings and infrastructure situated outside the boundaries of the project property. According to the guiding principles of the Living Building Challenge,

"projects have their own 'utility,' generating their own energy and processing their own waste. They (projects) more appropriately match scale to technology and end use, and result in greater self-sufficiency and security. Yet, the ideal scale for solutions is not always within a project's property boundary. Depending on the technology, the optimal scale can vary when considering environmental impact, first cost and operating costs. To address these realities, the Living Building Challenge has a Scale Jumping overlay to allow multiple buildings or projects to operate in a cooperative state — sharing green infrastructure as appropriate..."

For the UniverCity Childcare Centre, scale jumping came into play with a massive Habitat Exchange.

1 SOUTH ELEVATION

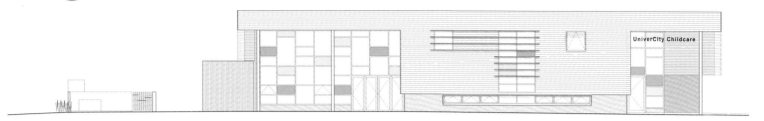

2 WEST ELEVATION

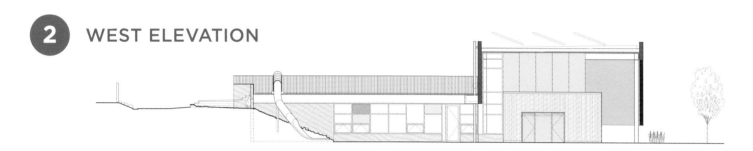

3 EAST ELEVATION

4 NORTH ELEVATION

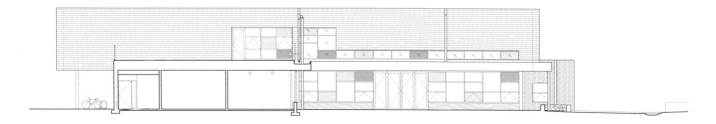

The Site Petal: COMMUNITY-CENTRIC

IMPERATIVE:
HABITAT EXCHANGE

The Challenge's Imperative for Habitat Exchange states, "For each acre of development, an equal amount of land must be set aside for at least 100 years as part of a habitat exchange." The UniverCity development site where the Centre is situated was part of an enormous scale jump that generously compensated for any habitat loss.

In 1996, SFU contributed nearly 800 acres (320 hectares) of land to the Burnaby Mountain Conservation Area in return for density and development rights on the remaining 160 acres (65 hectares) amounting to nearly five times the value of the Habitat Exchange mandate of the Living Building Challenge. While the Centre's overall footprint was small, thus limiting habitat compensation directly, the community of UniverCity as a grand-scale development

site, went far beyond maintaining the natural ecology of the area in addressing the Imperative.

The Habitat Exchange involving the vast majority of lands on Burnaby Mountain is notable, though that was not the only occasion where the project benefited from scale jumping. Big picture strategies would also inform solutions for the Energy Petal and the Water Petal at the Centre.

"Approximately 80 percent of the children attending the Centre live within walking distance."

KAREN VAUGHAN
UniverCity Childcare
Program Director

IMPERATIVE:
RESPONSIBLE SITE SELECTION

The Responsible Site Selection Imperative stipulates that a Living Building may not be located on, or adjacent to, sensitive ecological habitats such as wetlands, sand dunes, prime farmland, virgin prairie, old-growth forest or within a 100-year floodplain.

The location for the Childcare Centre readily met the Challenge's Site criteria; however, the Trust and the design team acknowledged that UniverCity's mountaintop locale was nonetheless, ecologically sensitive and should be regarded with the utmost foresight.

Indicative of the integrated nature of the Living Building Challenge, the team discovered repeatedly that no Petal had a stand-alone purpose. When it came to water-related issues, the Imperatives for the Site and the Water Petals intersected.

Surrounded by forested parkland and importantly, situated at the upper origin for two native watersheds, how the abundance of stormwater, typical of the West ("wet") Coast, would be addressed on the small site became another critical focal point for HCMA and the team of specialists. In fact, all planning and design decisions for the Centre hinged on strategies for reconciling the goals of all Petals — harmoniously.

The Site Petal: COMMUNITY-CENTRIC

> *"The significance of scale jumping in terms of the Living Building Challenge cannot be overlooked. In my mind, it's what makes it viable."*

DALE MIKKELSEN
Director of Development, SFU Community Trust

SUSTAINABLE CONDUCT — HEALTHY ON-SITE PRACTICES

Ledcor's project management team members took it upon themselves to delve deeper into what it meant to construct a Living Building so that their trades could effectively adapt to the rigors of the Standard. Developing Living Building specification tools was a big part of their engagement but encouraging healthy work-site behavior would also leave a legacy.

According to Ledcor's on-site personnel, everyone felt like pioneers, but it was not automatic from the beginning; rather, change came with yet another learning curve brought on by the high principles of the Living Building Challenge. The awareness that grew from adhering to all aspects of the Materials Petal (such as the Red List, Appropriate Sourcing and the challenge of achieving exceptional waste diversion) led to a construction site culture shift far beyond conventional practices. Not only did each design and construction decision become more mindful, measured against the tenets of the Challenge, actions transferred to a personal level. Individuals who were accustomed to smoking on the worksite were asked to curb their habit as not to affect the project or their peers. It took some doing but everyone involved was amenable to acting in the best interests of the future occupants.

84

"Working creatively with the site topography, we tucked the building into the existing slope and maximized the outdoor play space by making the rooftop accessible. This strategy provides clear views for supervision and a great opportunity to integrate a slide from the roof to the sand play area below."

JEFF CUTLER
Principal, space2place

IMPERATIVE:
LIMITS TO GROWTH

The Living Building Challenge's pre-requisite for limits to growth dictates that Living Building projects may only be built on greyfield or brownfield sites that have been previously developed. Most of the land adjacent to SFU prior to the development of UniverCity, particularly the community's western neighborhood, qualified as it was previously designated for surface parking, or was utilized to stockpile fill from the original construction of SFU. At the specific location of the Centre, the ground was composed of clean excavation material from past campus construction.

THE WATER PETAL

Model Hydrology

The Water Petal: **MODEL HYDROLOGY**

SUMMARY OF THE LIVING BUILDING CHALLENGE VERSION 1.3 WATER PETAL

Petal Intent

Scarcity of clean potable water is quickly becoming a serious issue in many countries around the world. Most regions of the United States and Canada have avoided the majority of these limitations and problems to date due to the presence of abundant fresh water, but highly unsustainable water use patterns and the continued drawdown of major aquifers portent significant problems ahead. The Challenge's prerequisites realign how people use water in the built environment, so that water is respected as a precious resource.

Petal Imperatives

• Net Zero Water
• Sustainable Water Discharge

"Water is the driving force in nature."

LEONARDO DA VINCI

IMPERATIVE:
NET ZERO WATER

The Living Building Challenge's Water Petal is one of the most significant for its immediate implications for a project — and for its upstream and downstream ramifications beyond the project site. The Imperatives of the Water Petal are intended to realign how people think about, and use, water in the built environment, regarding it as a precious resource.

The assignment of achieving net zero water at the individual site level inevitably leads to a broader-scale exploration of local, and even regional habitat. The essential value of water in terms of its quality, availability, and usage within the natural and built environments is drawn into the purview of the design team.

The Water Petal: MODEL HYDROLOGY

GRAVITY OF THE SITUATION

Located in the Pacific Maritime Ecozone, water is not considered to be in short supply at UniverCity.

Moist air masses crossing over the Pacific Ocean bring generous amounts of precipitation to Burnaby Mountain — particularly in the fall, winter, and spring seasons. Moderate temperatures with enduring sunny stretches and occasional rains characterize summer weather. Burnaby's annual precipitation of approximately 2000 mm per year is balanced out by a regionally enviable solar income of 2000 hours of sunshine annually. Much of the stormwater and snowmelt landing at SFU and UniverCity flows down the southern slopes of Burnaby Mountain feeding Burnaby's Eagle and Stoney Creek watersheds. Precipitation falling beyond the mountain ridge behind the Centre runs down the steep northern slopes of the mountain into the coastal fjord known as Burrard Inlet.

WATER CYCLE SCHEME

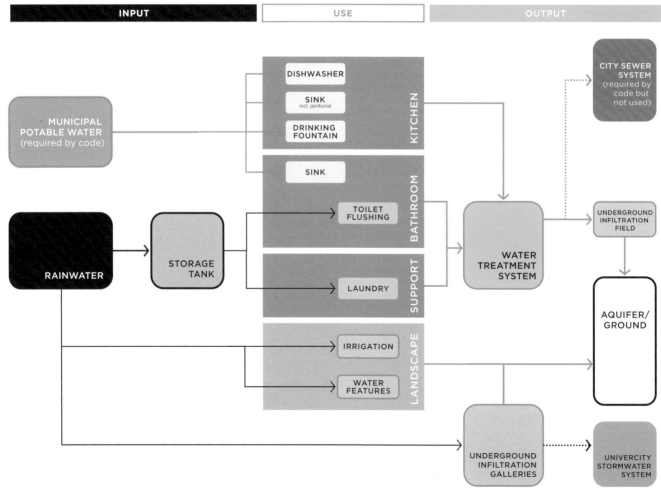

PROGRESSIVE COMMUNITY STORMWATER MANAGEMENT

The importance of managing water responsibly so that there is no harm caused to the surrounding habitat has not been lost on the community planners or the Centre's design team. With the centre being located at a higher elevation and adjacent to the Burnaby Mountain Conservation Area, one of Metro-Vancouver's largest wilderness preserves, the careful management of stormwater entering the watercourses is vital to the well-being of the extensive mountain and coastal ecosystems.

SFU Community Trust Development Director Dale Mikkelsen states unequivocally that, "When you live at the top of a mountain, at the very source of a watershed, how we use and care for water has far-reaching implications for every single organism." The Trust's work dedicated to water stewardship is a tangible example of a worldview shared by HCMA and proponents of the Challenge, acknowledging interdependence and valuing interconnectedness.

Along with the Burnaby Mountain neighborhood energy project that shares sustainable energy with the UniverCity Childcare Centre, the Centre is also an important part of UniverCity's community-wide stormwater management system. Rather than diverting large quantities of water away from the mountain's natural hydrological system into conventional drainage pipes or storm sewers, the development's comprehensive system functions to protect and preserve the natural watershed behavior by returning close to 100 percent of the local stormwater back to the ground, the creeks, and ultimately, the watershed.

Whenever possible the development's stormwater engineering infrastructure is configured to respect and maintain the right-of-way of water runoff with a natural, vegetated character in keeping with the local streams and tributaries in the area. Structures, paths, and bridges that may somehow interface with riparian areas are designed to carefully consider the stewardship of water and, by extension, the surrounding ecosystem. According to the Trust leadership, the objective of the innovative infrastructure is to sustain pre-development stormwater runoff quality and quantity such that salmon inhabiting streams at the bottom of Burnaby Mountain would not

be affected by the full service, modern, urban community that exists above — indeed, they would think that only unspoiled nature resides above their spawning grounds. The Simon Fraser University Official Community Plan details its commitment to safeguarding the integrity of water in the following excerpt of the Official Community Plan (OCP):

Rainwater collection tank

91

UNIVERCITY CHILDCARE CENTRE: AXONOMETRIC - EXPLODED

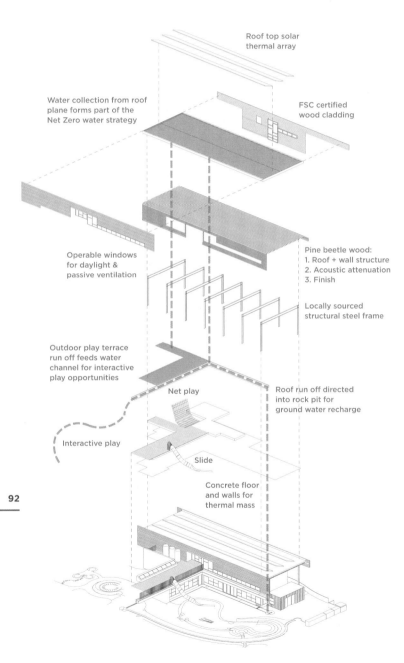

Roof top solar thermal array

Water collection from roof plane forms part of the Net Zero water strategy

FSC certified wood cladding

Operable windows for daylight & passive ventilation

Pine beetle wood:
1. Roof + wall structure
2. Acoustic attenuation
3. Finish

Locally sourced structural steel frame

Outdoor play terrace run off feeds water channel for interactive play opportunities

Net play

Roof run off directed into rock pit for ground water recharge

Interactive play

Slide

Concrete floor and walls for thermal mass

Simon Fraser University Official Community Plan
(Comprises part of the Official Community Plan for Burnaby)

3.2 Watercourses

3.2.1 Siting and design of development is to be consistent with the concept of Stream Stewardship, as set out by the Department of Fisheries and Oceans and the Ministry of Environment in the Stream Stewardship and Land Development Guidelines for the Protection of Aquatic Habitat documents.

3.2.2 Watercourses are to be managed in accordance with the Watercourse and Storm Water Management Plan referred to in Section 4.5. In general, existing watercourses are to be protected and maintained in an open, natural condition. Any proposed diversion, culverting or enclosure of minor watercourses is to be addressed on a comprehensive basis in this overall Management Plan prior to detailed subdivision planning, servicing design, and site planning within the Residential Neighbourhoods.

3.2.3 Building setbacks of 30 m (100 ft.) are to be provided to top of bank for major watercourses. The building setback can be reduced to 15 m (50 ft.) from top of bank for minor watercourses as determined through the Watercourse and Storm Water Management Plan, with consideration of localized variation possible based on special ecological circumstances.

3.2.4 Sediment control programs will be required prior to any site clearing, grading, development or servicing works being commenced.

Water abundance or not, the idea of reducing water demands at the Childcare Centre while preserving water quality beyond the Centre had a significant influence on how the design team went about reconciling the Imperatives of the Water Petal. There was no doubt that the pre-existence of UniverCity's advanced stormwater management protocol was beneficial to the Centre's design team for charting an innovative path toward addressing Sustainable Water Discharge. The ubiquitous nature of water lends itself perfectly to the Challenge's predilection for scale jumping solutions.

Should the Centre's rock pit reach capacity,
an overflow line will discharge runoff
to the community stormwater system

SUSTAINABLE WATER DISCHARGE — TOP DOWN ACCOUNTABILITY

The Challenge's Sustainable Water Discharge Imperative states that 100 percent of the stormwater and the building's water discharge must be managed on-site and integrated into a comprehensive system to meet the project's demands.

With this clear goal in mind, the design team employed a multifaceted approach to managing the Centre's stormwater. First, the team looked to absorb, then reduce the amount of excess water to a minimum by utilizing a high capacity rainwater catchment system. Rainwater is collected primarily from the rooftop, stored and treated, then reused for flushing the Centre's toilets and for janitorial services. The vegetated area of the lower roof also functions to mitigate some discharge, naturally holding moisture in the plant strata. Excess stormwater run-off is first directed to the infiltration gallery located underneath a play area, and in the event that the gallery reaches saturation, excess water then enters the community's master stormwater system. Overall, the Centre's water catchment system is capable of collecting and using approximately 300,000 liters annually.

93

Colorful, child-sized diversion valve — a "steering wheel" attached to a guardrail located next to the building on the rooftop deck that is both a functional device and an educational tool.

RAINWATER COLLECTION

Engineer Jean Sebastien Tessier submitted a Rain Water Capture and Treatment Failsafe Strategy Description to the City of Burnaby's Approvals Supervisor. This document included schematics, specifications and function details about each of the thirteen components involved in the system and outlined the design team's plan for storing and managing rainwater for flushing toilets and janitorial services at the Centre.

Precipitation collected from the higher roof (a 410m² water catchment area) drains into a cistern for storage, flowing through a motorized 3-way, two-position control valve through treatment filters to the pressure tank and PRV station. Water treated to a recreational grade, non-potable standard is then available for use at the Centre's water closets and janitorial sink. The unlined fiber-reinforced plastic tank has a total capacity of 45,000 litres. Rainwater from the lower green roof

runs off towards landscape water features around the building. The rainwater cistern is equipped with a booster pump package (two Grundfos submersible pumps in parallel for a total capacity of 60 gpm) that pressurizes the non-potable water supply.

In addition to landscape irrigation and some clever operational applications for using and reusing rainwater, the design team members dreamed up some very creative and delightful design elements to integrate water into the Childcare Centre's Reggio Emilia programming in the form of experiential waterplay.(see Waterplay — Nourishing the Senses, page 153). Interestingly, the design team has seen to it that water is utilized in intelligent and practical ways to service the needs of people and plants, as well as incorporating water's elemental contribution to education in the form of recreation for the children.

POSITION A
Water passes through Diverter into pipe below leading to the storage tank.

POSITION B
Water is diverted to the water canal to feed irrigation or water play features.

AIMING FOR WATER SELF-SUFFICIENCY

The Challenge required the Centre to deliver net zero water performance within its site boundaries at a minimum. The project design philosophy was to consider entire systems and do whatever possible to connect between all the performance areas of the Challenge, the Centre and the community.

Designing a well-balanced water cycle scheme that addressed all three levels of water quality within the Centre was a true exercise in integrated design. For the Centre, that meant coming up with a comprehensive system for a net zero solution that incorporated all requirements for potable water (for consumption, kitchen use and hand-washing), greywater effluent (drain runoff from various sinks, laundry, dishwasher and drinking fountain) and blackwater effluent (from toilet flushing and janitorial).

All plumbing fixtures at the Centre are low-flow fixtures. Water closets (4.8 lpf) are equipped with flush valves to avoid standing water in the system and bacterial growth. The lavatories are outfitted with high-efficiency (1.9 lpm), solar-powered faucets and the team selected a high-performance, low-consumption commercial dishwasher noting that commercial dishwashers use far less water than residential dishwashers.

95

> *"To trace the history of a river or a raindrop is also to trace the history of the soul, the history of the mind descending and arising in the body. In both, we constantly seek and stumble upon divinity, which like feeding the lake, and the spring becoming a waterfall, feeds, spills, falls, and feeds itself all over again."*

GRETEL EHRLICH
Islands, The Universe, Home

PURE INTENTIONS

According to Karen Marler, the design team's preliminary approach for achieving net zero water involved capturing rainwater, and innovatively treating blackwater on-site for reuse in irrigation and toilet flushing. Due diligence revealed that implementing an innovative closed loop water treatment system of this kind for the Centre would most likely lead to complex dealings with provincial, regional, and city regulatory officials. As with the Rainwater document, Tessier also submitted an in-depth Blackwater Treatment Failsafe Strategy Description to the City of Burnaby Planning Department that included schematics, specifications and function details about every component. Failsafe provisions conforming to code (including lift pump failure) were covered. However, as there was no established review process for projects of

this scale or typology, and no precedent to guide decisions for a chlorine-free solution derived from blackwater, an alternative tact was required that led back to the conventional practice of tapping the municipal potable water system.

This approach is currently accepted under the Living Building Challenge, provided the applicant has pursued every possible channel with local authorities for the use of captured water for possible uses. The developers of the Childcare Centre explored all options with the City and the local Health Authority, but were ultimately unable to receive permits for this level of treatment and re-use without the addition of a drip-feed chlorination at the end of the treatment cycle, which would then contravene the Red Listed materials in the Challenge.

SIMPLE, FLUID PROCESS

The design team looked to British Columbia-based ECOfluid Systems for a highly advanced biological wastewater treatment system for the Centre. ECOfluid's innovative Upflow Sludge Blanket Filtration (USBF™) bioreactor offered a simple, gravity flow process that was self-regulating and had no moving parts. USBF offers increased biological efficiency because all the processes are integrated within a compact bioreactor and, importantly, can be customized to meet the exacting requirements of the site. The compact

design of the UniverCity Childcare Centre USBF bioreactor, particularly important for this diminutive site, accommodates elevated peak flows and flow fluctuations automatically. The biomimetic USBF system also boasts reduced maintenance and operating costs and functions odor-free.

BLACKWATER TREATMENT

Regulatory requirements raised issues with blackwater treatment on-site. Officials were concerned that utilizing the Centre grounds as a septic field (instead of hard piping it away) may have health and water quality ramifications. Also, the Fraser Health Authority and the City of Burnaby currently require potable water to be chlorinated, conflicting with the Living Building Challenge's Imperatives as chlorine is listed on the Challenge's Materials Red List of hazardous chemicals, identified for its negative impact on human and ecosystem health. The team's original plan for reusing all water on-site was a no-go.

The design team anticipated a volume of approximately 2,500 litres of effluent per day, and directed all sanitary drainage below grade to the Centre's on-site bioreactor wastewater treatment system. After primary treatment and filtration in the bioreactor tank, discharge then flows to a series of ultraviolet (UV) disinfection units located inside the mechanical room. Discharge from the UV units provides clean, recreational grade water that meets the most stringent requirements of British Columbia's Ministry of Health. Finally, treated water is discharged to the infiltration gallery located in the northwestern corner of the grounds and is allowed to percolate the site providing below-grade irrigation. In the end, the design team had to limit the scope of blackwater use on-site, and return treated effluent to the ground via infiltration.

POTABLE WATER

For the Centre, reaching the ideal outcome for potable water use was ultimately dependent on what treatment methods were allowable by the governing codes. Regulatory and legal obstacles aside, the exploration of water treatment issues contributed to the building of lasting partnerships with local government to address conventional barriers to advancing the leading edge of sustainable design. Should regulatory requirements be amended in the future to allow non-chlorinated potable water, the Centre's innovative water infrastructure is in place. Until then, an exemption to allow for municipal water at the Centre has been granted by officials overseeing the Living Building Challenge.

USBF BIOREACTOR

Operation of a USBF™ plant is simple and self-regulating. Wastewater enters the anoxic compartment of the bioreactor where it mixes with activated sludge recycled from the bottom of the sludge filter. Agitated and moved in a controlled manner, the mixed liquor flows into the bioreactor's aerobic compartment. From the aerobic compartment the mixture of microbial cells and water enters the sludge filter at the bottom and, as it rises, upward velocity decreases until the flocs of cells become stationary and thus form a filtering media. A high degree of filtration efficiency is achieved as even particles with settling velocities too low to be removed by settling alone are filtered out. As the flocs become large and heavy by impact agglomeration, they descend to the bottom of the sludge filter and subsequently are recycled back into the anoxic zone. Filtered effluent overflows into a collection trough and is discharged from the system. Source: ECOfluid Systems, Inc.

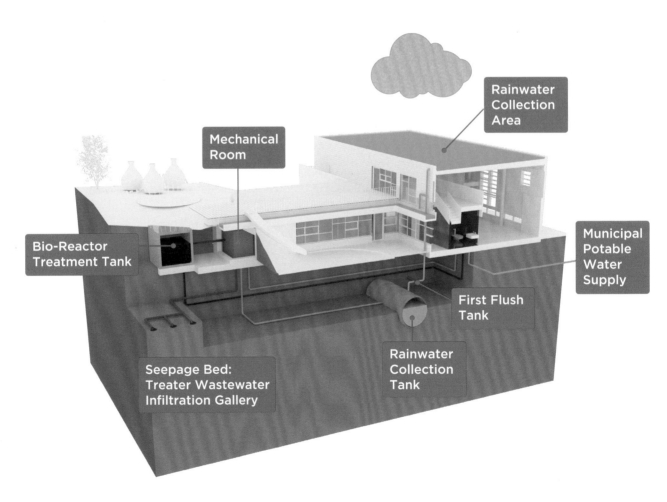

Rainwater Collection Area

Mechanical Room

Bio-Reactor Treatment Tank

Municipal Potable Water Supply

First Flush Tank

Seepage Bed: Treater Wastewater Infiltration Gallery

Rainwater Collection Tank

POTABLE WATER

Given the regulatory requirements, municipal water is used for potable uses in the project.

RAINWATER COLLECTION

Part of the project's water management strategy is to store rainwater on-site for flushing toilets. The collected rainwater from the higher roof area will flow into a cistern for storage (the water from the lower, green roof is directed towards landscape water features). The rainwater cistern is equipped with a booster pump package that provides pressurization for non-potable water supply to toilets.

BLACKWATER TREATMENT

With an anticipated volume of 2,500 litres/day, all building sanitary drainage will be directed to a treatment system which meets B.C. Ministry of Health Type 3 (most stringent requirement) on-site wastewater treatment standards. The process includes:

1. All building sanitary drainage will be directed to a below grade bioreactor tank

2. After primary treatment and filtration, the discharge flows to a series of UV disinfection units located inside the building mechanical room.

3. The discharge from these UV units will provide Level 3 Treatment.

4. The treated recreational grade water discharge then flows to the northwestern corner of the property and is dispersed below grade via an infiltration field.

STORMWATER MANAGEMENT

A multistage design strategy has been developed to deal with the building's stormwater runoff;

1. The rainwater collection system is the first step in absorbing and reducing stormwater runoff.

2. The vegetated area of the lower roof also contributes to reducing runoff.

3. When the cistern water level is high, the overflow line will direct flow into an on-site rock pit (infiltration field) which percolates water to the ground;

4. Should the rock pit start to overflow, an overflow line will discharge stormwater to the UniverCity stormwater system which is itself a community-scale system for environmentally responsible management of stormwater with no reliance on municipal infrastructure.

UPFLOW SLUDGE BLANKET FILTRATION (USBF®) BIOREACTOR PROCESS

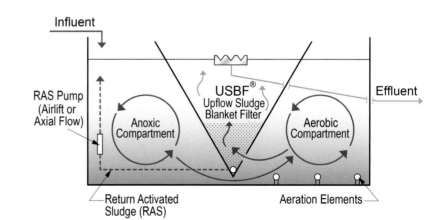

State of the art, self-regulating wastewater treatment bioreactor delivering high treatment efficiency, including biological nitrogen and phosphorus reduction. Filtered effluent overflows into a collection trough and is discharged to the infiltration gallery.

THE ENERGY PETAL

Powerful Exchanges

100

The Energy Petal: **POWERFUL EXCHANGES**

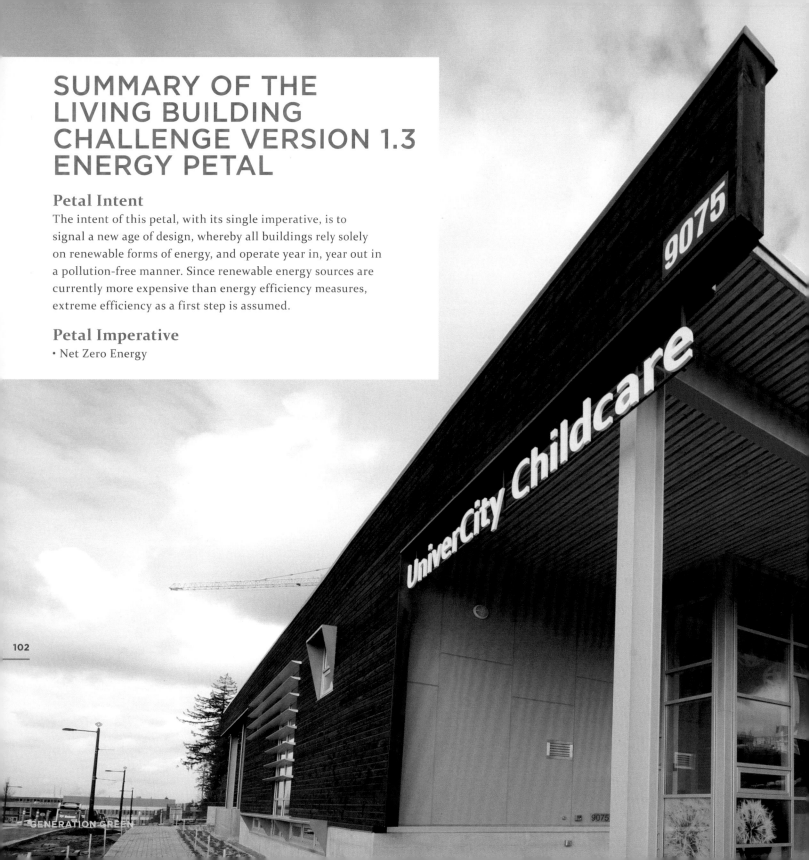

SUMMARY OF THE LIVING BUILDING CHALLENGE VERSION 1.3 ENERGY PETAL

Petal Intent

The intent of this petal, with its single imperative, is to signal a new age of design, whereby all buildings rely solely on renewable forms of energy, and operate year in, year out in a pollution-free manner. Since renewable energy sources are currently more expensive than energy efficiency measures, extreme efficiency as a first step is assumed.

Petal Imperative

• Net Zero Energy

> *"We will live in a world of relative scarcity compared to what was available in the 20th century, but we will be more connected and abundant from deeper connections to place and culture and a proper relationship with the natural world. We will rely on the human machine and 'current solar income' to propel us forward, and enjoy the vitality that follows."*

JASON F. MCLENNAN
The Originator of the
Living Building Challenge

IMPERATIVE:
NET ZERO ENERGY

The Living Building Challenge Version 1.3 states that 100 percent of a building's energy needs must be supplied by on-site renewable energy on a net annual basis.

The Standard further stipulates that the scope of the building's energy includes all electricity, and heating and cooling requirements, noting that the energy system may be grid-tied or off the grid.

The Challenge identifies renewable energy technologies as photovoltaics, wind turbines, water-powered microturbines, methane from composting only, direct geothermal or fuel cells powered by hydrogen generated from renewably powered electrolysis. With these formidable parameters in mind, the design team set forth to solve the Energy Petal at the Centre.

(RE)EVALUATING ENERGY

In terms of its singular and precise purpose, the Challenge's Energy Petal is straightforward — Living Buildings must achieve net zero energy.

According to most seasoned design professionals, Mikkelsen and Marler among them, advancing a reasonably well-designed building to net zero energy is not overly difficult when land is abundant and funding for technology is relatively unconstrained. A project simply needs to utilize sufficient solar arrays to meet the energy demands of the building.

The Centre did not have the luxury of unconstrained funds for purchasing copious solar equipment, nor was the Centre's diminutive site or architecture

suitable to host outsized solar arrays necessary to fully meet the energy needs of the facility. Even if funds for extra solar technology had been available, space was limited on the grounds to install more panels beyond what was planned for the rooftop. Notably, the design team was not interested in compromising the programmatic goals for the project tied to the high-quality educational outdoor play spaces for the sake of net zero energy alone. Holding to the rigorous standards for design and education, team members were stuck.

COMMUNITY APPROACH

In order for the UniverCity Childcare Centre to best solve for net zero energy, a thorough investigation of appropriate technologies and resources was required. The design team determined that although considerable progress had been made to advance renewable energy technologies there was still a need for a greater yield from these systems, plus new methods to store the energy generated.

These technical challenges, together with the current cost of the various high-tech systems available, are major limitations for deep green projects like the UniverCity Childcare Centre with high-performance energy goals. And, as the case is with all but the generously funded demonstration projects, best-in-class renewable technologies and the Centre's local assets needed to be reconciled within the hard and fast boundaries of the project's conservative budget.

UniverCity is a leading edge sustainable development with a contemporary infrastructure designed to respond to the changing needs of the community, so it made perfect sense to look for answers to the Centre's challenges by integrating systems within the community. The Trust took stock of the resources in the vicinity of the Centre that offered some sort of potential synergy. Dale Mikkelsen, familiar with the unconventional yet creative design approach known as scale jumping fostered by the Living Building Challenge, recognized the prospective power of community partnerships.

Thanks to the elevated vision of the Trust, HCMA and the SFU educational community, the Centre was predestined to be deeply integrated socially and educationally with UniverCity so connecting the building physically to share energy was a natural fit. Otherwise, the Centre would have had to meet the year-round domestic hot water and heating needs of the building through solar thermal and space heating options. On top of that approach they would have had to go to a PV solution to address electrical plug loads. According to Mikkelsen (and backed against his pre-cast budget), the costs of energy technology would have made the project a non-starter. It was this fundamental shift in thinking about energy that allowed the project to continue.

Emboldened by the expanded scope of possibilities, the Trust and HCMA delved into an exploration of community-scale opportunities to resolve the Energy Petal. The exploration pointed to a network sharing arrangement with a neighborhood energy utility. Not only would involvement with a localized energy utility be ideal for UniverCity and the Childcare Centre, it would offer a dynamic solution for integration with a safe, reliable and decentralized power grid founded on renewable energy which dovetails perfectly with the guiding principles of the Living Building Challenge.

In advance of the Childcare Centre project, staff members at the SFU Community Trust were already engaged in dreaming of an alternative energy supply for the UniverCity neighborhood as it continued to grow and incrementally increase its sustainability initiatives. Intent on applying a Scale Jumping design overlay at the community level, and having a sizable carbon reduction goal for UniverCity, the Trust weighed

its options. Unlike large institutions, such as hospitals with substantial budgets and expert facility operations departments, the Trust was an office comprised of seven people, not one engineer among them. The Trust leadership quickly realized that the best course of action was to share the prospective neighborhood connectivity concept with the energy marketplace to gauge interest in some form of a neighborhood energy utility (NEU) partnership.

The Trust issued a Request for Expressions of Interest (EOI) to public and private utility partners that called for third-party title and operation, BC Utilities Commission regulated fees guaranteeing equitable rates present and future, and that offered a technology that would reduce greenhouse gases by no less than 50 percent. The EOI yielded six responses from various utility providers that the Trust subsequently narrowed down to three from which they requested formal proposals.

The bid from private energy firm Corix Energy Services emerged as the top choice, meeting the Trust's conditions to design, build and operate a long-term and environmentally responsible centralized energy system on Burnaby Mountain. Corix conducted comprehensive technical evaluations, including air quality testing, plus a detailed cost analysis. The resulting solution proposed by Corix was to phase in a modular biomass facility that, when completed, would be capable of providing the expanding neighborhood with domestic hot water and heat, while saving an estimated 1,750 tonnes of greenhouse gas emissions annually. The NEU solution to provide thermal energy would help new buildings at UniverCity exceed the City of Burnaby's energy performance requirements and also mitigated the costly duplication of infrastructure that would have otherwise been required if UniverCity had elected to go with the regional energy provider.

Centralized Systems:
The Centre's Mechanical Room

ENERGY-SYNERGY (THE DISTRICT UTILITY ENERGY INTERFACE)

The Childcare Centre is directly connected to the Corix Utilities underground distribution network; however, the Centre's relationship with the utility differs from other benefactors in that the Centre is designed to operate as a net contributor to the energy grid on an annual basis.

"In terms of energy efficiency, it wasn't just about asking the buildings to do more, it was about asking the community to do more."

DALE MIKKELSEN
Director of Development,
SFU Community Trust

The Burnaby Mountain district energy system now efficiently produces and delivers reliable and economical heat and hot water to hundreds of residences in more than six buildings from a single, highly efficient energy source in the community. This design eliminates the need for each building to have its own boilers, hot water storage tanks, and other associated equipment, thereby lowering operating costs for building owners and increasing thermal comfort and hot water supply. In addition to the capital savings attributed to the communal system,

expansion to the Corix facility will ultimately replace the antiquated gas boiler that serves the university's institutional buildings, further curtailing related greenhouse gas emissions in the order of an additional 10,000 tonnes annually (a minimum 70 percent reduction in campus GHG emissions). The characteristic benefits of Canada's largest neighborhood-level energy utility are genuinely impressive — and so too is its synergistic relationship with the UniverCity Childcare Centre Living Building.

"The mechanical system is very, very passive and, in turn, a very cost-effective solution."

KAREN MARLER
Principal, HCMA

POWERING THE CENTRE

A portion of the Centre's rooftop area accommodates the solar collectors while other sections of the structure are covered by green roof and outdoor play areas. The Centre's solar array functions as the building's energy source complemented by the building's concrete foundation, floors and walls that add significant thermal mass to the structure, thereby reducing the energy required to heat and cool the building.

The Centre's solar collectors produce hot water year round for energy re-use through exportation to the neighborhood energy utility (NEU). The south-facing rooftop solar array consists of thirty-six Sunda Seido 1-16 solar hot water collectors (2.8 m² each) that are capable of generating approximately 67kW of heat and producing approximately 69,000 kW-hr of energy annually.

ENERGY EXCHANGE

Thermally generated hot water from the Centre's solar array is pumped into the NEU and the Centre draws back what energy it needs. Domestic hot water from the utility, in turn, supplies the kitchen and washroom facilities, as well as feeding the in-floor radiant heating system that spans the entire 530 m² (5,700 sf) indoor floor area . The premise of the energy equation is that the Centre's solar array, over time, will provide sufficient energy to the communal system, balancing at, or below, net zero energy. This give and take energy relationship also offsets the Centre's electrical loads. Put another way, if the net zero energy requirements for the Centre are to be met annually, it needs to over-subscribe solar-thermal energy.

ENERGY

The project energy strategy is threefold:

A. REDUCING DEMAND

- South-facing glazing to harvest solar energy in winter

- The north part of the building, where passive solar heating is not available, takes advantage of the site's natural slope and is buried underground

- Triple glazing is used for reducing heat loss through the envelope

- In-floor radiant heating in combination with concrete floors provide thermal energy storage minimizing peak energy demand

- No cooling is provided; the large doors and operable windows will allow for natural ventilation in summer

- Fan energy has been minimized by using displacement ventilation combined with heat recovery

- Offices are provided with natural ventilation only

B. NET ZERO ENERGY

The project achieves Net Zero Energy through the concept of "scale-jumping," i.e. the synergy between a single building and its host community. The oversized solar collector array on the roof provides more energy than required to heat the building, effectively offsetting the building's power consumption (in other words, on an annual net basis the total kWh of energy generated by the solar thermal system will offset the total kWh of all types of energy consumed by the building)

C. ENERGY FROM RENEWABLE SOURCES ONLY

- The on-site energy generation is through the roof-mounted evacuated tube solar collectors

- The UniverCity's district energy system is a bio-energy system (a renewable source as well)

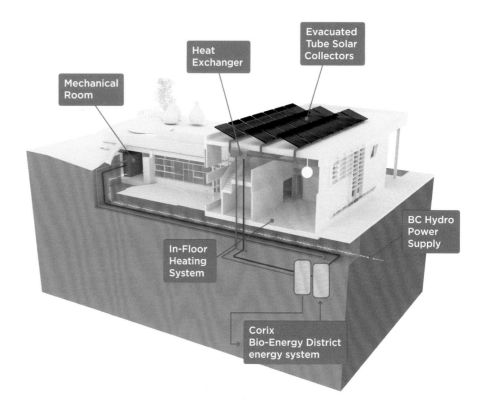

Mechanical Room

Heat Exchanger

Evacuated Tube Solar Collectors

In-Floor Heating System

BC Hydro Power Supply

Corix Bio-Energy District energy system

109

Durable do-it-all softwood panels offer additional
daylighting and sound-dampening acoustical benefits.

110

"Passive and sustainable mechanical designs contributed significantly to meeting the goals of the Living Building Challenge."

KEVIN HYDES
CEO, Integral Group

ENERGY REQUIREMENTS OF THE CENTRE

HCMA's "simple is better" approach to creating design efficiencies for the project carried forth in their energy strategy for heating, cooling and plug load reduction. Facilitating an abundance of daylight was an important design element for the Childcare Centre. Ample glazing permits a proliferation of natural light to enter activity rooms and community spaces, offsetting the need for extensive illumination via electrical lighting. Complementary to the energy savings afforded by the daylighting scheme, HCMA employed a passive cooling strategy as another measure for keeping occupants comfortable and energy expenditures low.

The Centre's mechanical systems are uncomplicated, taking up nominal interior space and drawing relatively little electrical power.

The mechanical and technological equipment necessary to support the largely passive cooling methodology, plus lighting fixtures and controls, and a modest number of occupancy and CO_2 sensors, define the plug loads within the Centre.

Kitchen appliances and office equipment, such as computers and telecommunications devices, were selected specifically for their energy-saving attributes. Accent lighting for the purpose of wayfinding is embedded in select outdoor surfaces around the Centre such as the front entrance and the upper deck area. Functional and modish, these self-sustaining LED glass tiles do not contribute to plug loads. With all the heating requirements for the building being met through the radiant in-floor heating system, the overall energy requirements for the Centre are trimmed down to a minimum.

"*For the children, green is the new normal. Growing up green is the way I think of it. These children have some crazy advantages when it comes to understanding the relationship between the built and natural environment.*"

JAY LIN
Architect, HCMA

112

TOMORROW'S ENERGY STRATEGY, TODAY

Through the Living Building Challenge and its Living Communities program, the International Living Future Institute promotes the implementation of solutions beyond the individual project scale that maximize ecological benefits while maintaining self-sufficiency at the city block, neighborhood, or community scale. The UniverCity Childcare Centre Living Building, and the UniverCity community have become an evocative working model for present and future sustainable developments.

Despite the limitations of the project's fixed budget, established long before the Trust targeted the ambitious Living Building Challenge, and compounded further by the confined size of the site, the Trust and HCMA resolved to find solutions for energy, site and water despite apparent regulatory and design barriers. In actuality it was the trials of overcoming difficult conditions that propelled the design team to explore outside of the box for alternative solutions for various Petals such as Energy.

In the end, it was the scale jumping design overlay that played the most critical role in making what first appeared to be a blue-sky project, possible and affordable. Not only are the environmental and economical benefits of supplying practical, renewable energy to a neighborhood network infrastructure of highly efficient buildings paying off at a community level, the UniverCity Childcare Centre Living Building is functioning as an emblematic precedent, reminiscent of the spirit of positive change embedded within the Trust, the design team and the Living Building Challenge.

THE INDOOR QUALITY PETAL

Creating Healthy Interior Spaces

115

SUMMARY OF THE LIVING BUILDING CHALLENGE VERSION 1.3 INDOOR QUALITY PETAL

Petal Intent

Most buildings provide far less than ideal conditions for maximum health and productivity. As comfort decreases, environmental impact often increases, as people find inefficient and wasteful solutions to improve their physical environment. The intent of these prerequisites is not to address all of the potential ways that an interior environment may be compromised, but to focus on best practices to create a healthy interior environment.

116

Petal Imperatives

• A Civilized Environment
• Healthy Air: Ventilation
• Healthy Air: Source Control

IMPERATIVE:
A CIVILIZED ENVIRONMENT THAT HONORS NATURE

The Living Building Challenge envisions that the overall environment of Living Buildings will contribute holistically to the physical and emotional well-being of the occupants, their families and communities and, by extension, demonstrates reverence for the natural environment. The intent of the Indoor Quality Petal is to ensure that the indoor environments of Living Buildings are naturally healthy, clean and civilized at the very least, though embodied within the spirit of the Challenge is the belief that Living Buildings foster a deeper connection to nature.

117

Living Building indoor-outdoor structures and character are intended to honor nature's intelligent functions and elegant form and the interior environments are to welcome in natural light and fresh air — free of harmful chemicals — facilitating thermal comfort and visual delight. In this respect, aspects of the Materials Petal, the Beauty Petal and the Indoor Quality Petal are integrated within Living Building designs.

Expert design practitioners and green building advocates alike have noted that despite the best designs, technology and intentions instilled within deep green architecture, it can be difficult to ensure that buildings remain vibrant for people in the long term. A major concern associated with exemplary buildings not functioning as designed are that some sensory qualities such as healthy indoor air, thermal control and visual delight may be compromised due to the unpredictable manner

in which people use and maintain these buildings. In order to minimize inefficiencies, some high-performance buildings utilize high-tech systems and controls to eliminate the possibility of human error, or use design elements such as inoperable windows (or a bare minimum of windows) to maintain the integrity of the building envelope. Demanding as it may be to preserve the healthy conditions created through the rigorous process of designing for the Living Building program, the purpose-driven Imperatives of the Challenge point toward long-term optimal conditions for occupants — with the occupants. The UniverCity Childcare Centre Living Building, comprised of thoughtful design elements that acknowledge the need for a balance between mechanical and human controls, puts the health and experience of the occupants first, thereby defining the Centre's ongoing commitment to a Civilized Environment.

> *"In terms of the quality of the space and healthy attributes (air, light, materials), this building stands in stark contrast to traditional childcare buildings."*
>
> **KAREN VAUGHAN**
> UniverCity Childcare
> Program Director

IMPERATIVE:
HEALTHY AIR — VENTILATION, FRESH AND COOL

Taking advantage of fluid dynamics and the ventilation stratification effect within the Centre's tall spaces, the design team opted for a trickle vent system to facilitate natural ventilation, effectively mitigating the need for an expensive cooling system.

Carbon dioxide (CO_2) sensors automatically open vents located in the upper reaches of the building allowing for fresh air to flow into the Centre, replenishing indoor air while dissipating excess CO_2 accordingly when levels are elevated. The lower windows in the mezzanine area, when opened, allow for air mixing and cross ventilation that naturally refreshes the facility. The Centre's low voltage bathroom fans continually draw fresh air through the building, promoting continual circulation, expelling stale air out fan exhausts, and thus enhancing ventilation and general air

quality throughout. The free cooling effect via natural convection during the warmer summer months contributes to the thermal delight of occupants and mitigates potential costs associated with the purchasing and powering of conventional HVAC equipment. The Centre's community spaces are outfitted with operable windows to optimize air manipulation and the trickle vents may also be adjusted by staff members wishing to fine-tune indoor thermal conditions.

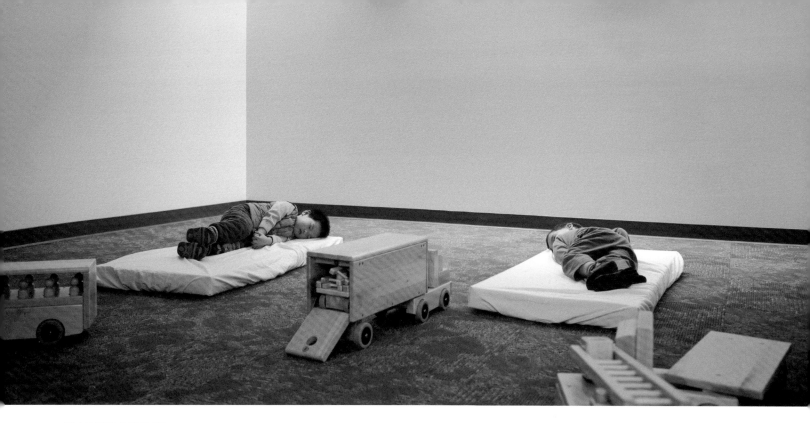

IMPERATIVE:
HEALTHY AIR — SOURCE CONTROL, MANAGING AIR QUALITY

The Living Building Challenge's Materials Petal addressed the introduction of toxic building materials, products, paints and finishes into the Centre. However, at the post-occupancy stage it is the responsibility of the occupants to maintain the healthy conditions such as cleanliness and air quality of the building.

Climatic conditions on Burnaby Mountain, be it altitude, air temperature, humidity, sunlight, rain, snow or wind, possess the innate power to influence life within the Centre. HCMA acknowledged the potential effects of varying environmental elements with clever design, embracing what was, at most times, favorable conditions (fresh air and ample daylight), and tempering naturally-occurring outdoor circumstances (cold air, dust and debris) that could compromise the indoor quality of the Centre. Following criteria set by the Challenge, the design team made sure the Childcare Centre's entryways were equipped with an external dirt track-in system, including an internal arrangement contained within the separate, adjacent, entry area.

The kitchen galley, bathrooms, office space, janitorial and chemical storage spaces are separately ventilated. Linking back to the rigorous process the team underwent for tackling the Materials Petal, the team made sure that all interior finishes, paints and adhesives associated with the project complied with SCAQMD 2007/2008 standards required for meeting the Healthy Air: Source Control prerequisite of the Indoor Quality Petal. Similarly, all other interior materials such as the Centre's flooring and millwork was painstakingly vetted and selected to meet the comprehensive California Standard 01350 for IAQ emissions. Predictably, the UniverCity Childcare Centre is a non-smoking facility.

119

120

*"The Challenge outlines the ideal end result but provides
no hard and fast rules on how to attain that result.
With our trades working on the Centre, we implemented
a detailed indoor air quality plan that included very specific
information, such as VOC limits, to make it easier for them
to understand the requirements for Living Buildings."*

MARSHA GENTILE
Construction Sustainability Specialist,
Ledcor Construction

HEALTHY ATTENTION TO DETAIL

Free-standing, movable furnishings including desks, benches,
chairs, electronic equipment, tables, shelves and bookcases
are excluded from the Living Building Challenge and therefore
from Red List tracking requirements central in the Materials
Petal. That exclusion allowance did not stop Karen Vaughan,
the original Program Coordinator for the Centre, from
adhering to a purchasing protocol that stayed true to the
intent of the Challenge's mandate for healthy elements.

Vaughan corresponded with HCMA materials expert Kourosh
Mahvash in investigating non-toxic decor options for the
Centre and then purchased furniture, educational tools and
toys based on the strict guidelines of the Challenge's Materials
Red List. Cleaning supplies, hand towels (reusable) and the
like, were similarly vetted. Centre staff considered the process
valuable for the genuine introspection into what children are
exposed to on a daily basis, under normal circumstances.

PASSING THE PARENT TEST

The Living Building process required everyone connected to the project to be involved in making important decisions. Immersed in exploring the details of Challenge-related decisions, HCMA conducted some intense scrutiny of their own in selecting the right flooring material for the Centre. Originally, the team had specified a premium flooring product made from recycled tires that was available regionally and met the technical requirements of the Materials Red List. The project architect, Kathleen Robertson, a mother herself, noticed that the product was off gassing a particular odor that most likely related back to the original tire material and/or the manufacturing process. HCMA designers, all parents themselves, considered the fact that children were going to be walking, sometimes crawling around on the floor. With this understanding they knew that personally and professionally they could not install a product that was possibly off gassing toxic compounds so they nixed the use of the original product and sought out a healthier alternative, holding yet again to the higher standard of "doing the right thing."

"Even when considering the furnishings, the aesthetics, along with healthy materials, was always at the forefront in my mind."

KAREN VAUGHAN
UniverCity Childcare
Program Director

121

DESIGN AS TEACHER

The opportunities to observe, interact, and experience nature were possible both indoors and outdoors at the Centre. While occupancy sensors for lighting are utilized in some locations, HCMA chose not to install sensors in all situations at the Centre. Karen Marler noted that while sensors draw some electrical power, that was not the reason to omit the automated devices in some situations. Rather, HCMA recognized the opportunity to teach the children about energy usage via the direct use of conventional light switches. The thinking behind using the low-tech controls was that if, through simple monitoring, it could be demonstrated to the children that when all the lights were off, on a sunny day for instance, they could see the energy savings firsthand.

The team also incorporated other elements into the design of the Centre that facilitate tangible experiences as a means to educate the children by identifying and providing learning zones suitable for active, social, creative, nature and fantasy-oriented play experiences. The cause and effect of turning lights on and off or feeling the warmth of the winter sun through window glass, are a big part of the integrated thinking indicative of just about every aspect of the Centre. Opportunities exist for the children to explore their world with their senses in just about every aspect of the Centre. For example, diverting water and observing the effects is a prime example of nature-related outdoor education while understanding the source and the value of water, air and light are ongoing, lifelong lessons experienced by the children at the Centre.

123

THE MATERIALS PETAL

Healthy Design and Construction

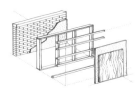

The Materials Petal: **HEALTHY DESIGN AND CONSTRUCTION**

SUMMARY OF THE LIVING BUILDING CHALLENGE VERSION 1.3 MATERIALS PETAL

Petal Intent

The intent of the Materials Petal is to induce a successful materials economy that is non-toxic, transparent and socially equitable. The Imperatives aim to remove the worst known offending materials and practices. When impacts can be reduced but not eliminated, there is an obligation not only to offset the damaging consequences associated with the construction process, but also to strive for corrections in the industry.

Petal Imperatives

- Materials Red List
- Responsible Industry
- Appropriate Materials/Services Radius
- Leadership in Construction Waste
- Construction Carbon Footprint

126

"There's a temptation to get caught up in trying to interpret the minute details of various postings and what they mean for your own project. But this was not the way to go or what the Institute was directing us to do. What it comes down to is doing what makes sense in terms of sustainability. Approaching the Challenge this way made decision making much easier."

KOUROSH MAHVASH
Sustainable Research Leader, HCMA

SUSTAINABLE STRATEGY

Anticipating that designing and constructing the UniverCity Childcare Centre to be one of the country's first Living Buildings was not going to be "just another day at the office," HCMA closely evaluated the ramifications of addressing the requirements of all the Petals.

In-depth analysis led them to believe that meeting the Challenge was achievable, though Water and Materials were "difficult but possible". In order to meet the Imperatives of each Petal, the team decided that the best course of action was to adhere to a strategy that emphasized elegant solutions and a simple palette of materials over an involved high-tech methodology. The Centre's uncomplicated structural composite design of steel I-beam framing and integrated wood panel system was effective evidence of their unencumbered approach to Living Building design.

"Toxic chemicals and compounds are pervasive in building products, endangering human health and the resilience of our ecosystems. They not only harm building occupants, they cause damage all along their life cycle. Despite a growing mountain of research demonstrating the detrimental impact of toxic building materials and increasing public awareness of this fact, change has been slow."

AMANDA STURGEON
Vice President, ILFI and Director of the Living Building Challenge

INITIATING CHANGE

If "doing the right thing" had become the unofficial motto of the project, "changing the way things are done" was the maxim. **Not only did the team enthusiastically engage in an exceedingly comprehensive integrated design process in order to meet the rigorous demands of the project, team members examined every aspect of the work, holistically, through the lens of the Living Building Challenge.**

While the targets outlined for many of the Petals of the Challenge were straightforward (such as net zero energy and water) and all welcomed by the design team, the framework of Imperatives for the Materials Petal was exposing some real world, industry-wide shortcomings connected to product availability and transparency. In actuality, they discovered that "doing the right thing" by way of selecting the healthiest of building materials for the Centre, was a demanding task because complete product information listing various ingredients, compounds and chemicals was remarkably hard to come by.

It became apparent to HCMA and the consultant team that many product manufacturers, when pressed, could share very little information about the ingredients contained in their building products. While some suppliers were familiar with documentation for LEED projects, few companies had ever been subjected to the level of scrutiny associated with supplying products for a Living Building.

In order for the design team, the owner, and the construction contractor to make sound decisions for avoiding toxins when designing and constructing the Centre, the fundamental qualities of all potential materials had to be called into question. Lying at the heart of the Materials Petal is the ILFI's provocative Red List — a growing inventory of persistent toxic materials and chemicals deemed harmful to all life forms, including humans.

IMPERATIVE:
MATERIALS RED LIST

The intent of the Red List Imperative is to eliminate from buildings, and ultimately the market, the worst in-class materials and chemicals with the greatest negative impact to human and ecosystem health. Through this Imperative, the aim of the ILFI is to raise awareness and broadly influence the building industry's manufacturing and procurement processes through proactive and constructive communication between manufacturers, specifiers and consumers.

Living Building Project teams are encouraged to use Declare (the ILFI's product ingredients disclosure program and database) to source products (www.declareproducts.com). Declare listings and other third-party materials disclosure programs, all seeking transparency in the name of health, are at the leading edge of a monumental undertaking — the cataloging of countless products available for the building and construction industry.

The team's primary objective was to reconcile the stringent requirements of the Challenge's Red List, avoiding all toxic products and substances to be utilized in the construction and finishing of the Centre. The deeper their investigation went into available products for the built environment, the more exhaustive the search became. For HCMA, Ledcor and the Trust, it became more evident that Materials was to be the most formidable Petal for the Centre, and that the Red List functioned as a veritable test for virtually every design decision. As it turned out, the Imperatives of the Materials

Petal influenced literally everything at the Centre — inclusive of its architecture, programming and its culture. A cultural or behavioral shift for on-site workers is detailed in the **Leadership in Construction Waste** section below.

HCMA held Living Building Sustainability meetings regularly throughout the project to assess all issues that were arising through the process. Detailed dialogue about materials was required as tender documents were being prepared, and at each stage of the project. Numerous and ongoing conversations addressing Materials and the related Imperatives formed a common, often complex narrative as sourcing suitable products proved to be difficult.

After the building contractor, Ledcor Construction, was selected, the need for yet deeper integration became apparent. HCMA's Sustainability Research Leader and one of Canada's leading materials experts, Kourosh Mahvash, became involved in every

aspect of the project, and HCMA architect Jay Lin was tasked with the formidable job of overseeing and implementing the protocol for construction documentation. Frequent communications with the contractor to verify product compliance became commonplace as no one wanted to leave anything to chance. According to Marsha Gentile, the Ledcor Construction staffer charged with project documentation, finding solutions necessitated regular communications between all parties, day after day.

According to HCMA, Ledcor Construction had a strong team in place that was deeply invested in meeting the Challenge. To that end, Ledcor and their trades were willing to go to great lengths to unearth Red List-free products for the betterment of the Centre. Ledcor's diligence included frequent communication with suppliers and manufacturers, and notably, the development of various Living Building reference guides tailored for the trades that spelled out specifications in no uncertain terms. These pragmatic reference documents facilitated procurement as well as

process, going as far as providing guidelines for employee conduct on-site as it related back to working on a Living Building project.

Most all of the details for protocol and procurement circled back to HCMA for a meticulous double, and triple-check, to assure compliance with the Challenge. That same thorough attention to Red List specifics extended to all the consultants.

Regarding the Red List as the definitive measure, HCMA fielded and vetted each materials query to verify whether products were safe for inclusion in the Centre's construction. Mahvash poured over manufacturers' published product information, Materials Safety Data Sheets (MSDS) and ingredient lists in order to determine whether or not Red List chemicals and compounds were present. When answers were not evident in the published literature, candid communications with manufactures' technical staff followed. The approvals process, often difficult because of its convoluted, sometimes guarded nature, continued through to the final days of construction.

"We all realized that the process was all about common sense. Whether it's Red List or wasting water... just don't do it."

JAY LIN
Architect, HCMA

131

"My lasting impression of the project is not the challenges we faced but the inspiration we've fostered amongst the team, and brought to the community. My greatest hope is that the children attending the Centre follow in our footsteps, considering STEM fields (science, technology, engineering, and mathematics) to continue to develop sustainable solutions for our society."

CHARLIE YAO
Engineer-in-Training, MMM Group

SHORT STORIES WITH BIG IMPACTS

Initially, the Living Building Challenge appears to be another green building program but to those people involved with the Living Building Challenge, it is much more than a green building standard. Rather, the Challenge is a catalyst for transforming how things are done. Due diligence on the part of the UniverCity Childcare Centre team in vetting materials definitely led to some ultra-green solutions for the Centre.

FLOORING: At first, HCMA chose a tire-derived, recycled rubber flooring option from the original tender package; however, as they learned more about the more obscure chemical properties of the product, serious second thoughts emerged. When HCMA looked deeper into the manufacturing of tire-derived rubber flooring, then the life-cycle processes of recycling tires, they decided that the toxic by-products were not anything they wanted placed in close proximity to the children who would be walking, tumbling and playing on the Centre's floors day in, day out. Instead, the team made the conscious decision to raise the bar higher than what had been deemed acceptable, choosing a rubber-based product that was of the highest quality they could find. Again, the team's assessment and actions followed the unofficial project motto that had effectively become the pervading refrain for the Centre, "To do the right thing."

Other products were similarly scrutinized. A decision to avoid the use of concrete containing fly ash was reached in a similar fashion. However well-intended a by-product's creation may have been initially, HCMA thought it better to discourage the use of any material with a possible toxic legacy.

ELECTRICAL: Having previously not worked on a project with the same rigorous standards as a Living Building project, electrical contractor MMM Group had never had reason to communicate directly with a manufacturer (let alone the president of an electrical supply company) about the composition of electrical products utilized in plying their trade. However, in order to fulfill the specifications necessitated by the Challenge, details about electrical components normally considered acceptable within the trade had to be closely examined. MMM, now Red List aware, discovered that most wiring commonly available is covered by polyvinyl chloride (PVC), a compound strictly forbidden by the Challenge's stringent Red List of banned toxic materials. Despite market-wide constraints and instead of applying for an exemption with the ILFI, MMM set about searching for alternative PVC-free wiring products and sources.

The design plans featured easily accessible communication systems and flexible power systems tailored to meet the various needs of the Centre's occupants. Regarding wiring solutions, there were a few considerations. For power distribution, MMM relied on AC-90 cable that utilized cross-linked polyethylene as an insulator. The main challenge was for data cabling, and the team found a product that incorporated high-density polyethylene (HDPE) for insulation and non-halogenated polyolefin for the jacketing.

In standard practice PVC is also typically used for underground conduit; though for the Centre, the decision was made to go with a more expensive fiberglass product in lieu of PVC.

FINISHES: Tasked with the necessity of meeting HCMA's painting specifications for the Centre, the millworking company ended up not only evaluating the potential toxicity of materials used in their craft but also the actual processes of manufacturing. Typically, a well-ventilated spray booth is utilized for applying finishes and lacquers so that personnel are protected from inhaling air-borne volatiles. However workers, now Red List conscious, realized that once the finished material was back in the shop for cutting and sanding those same particulates they were guarding against were now being released back into the air. Abidance to the specifications of the Living Building Challenge spurred awareness that led to new, healthier, industry practices for the millworkers and, hopefully, to lasting change.

IMPERATIVE:
RESPONSIBLE INDUSTRY

The intent of the Challenge's Responsible Industry Imperative is to reduce the damaging environmental and social impacts related to industries dependent on natural resource extraction including stone, rock, metal and timber. British Columbia is remarkably beautiful for its abundance of wild places; however, the perspective of ample wilderness viewed from a commercial perspective amounts to opportunities for natural resource extraction — in many cases to supply materials for the built environment.

Favorable forest and climatic conditions have led to a Mountain Pine Beetle epidemic in the Pacific Northwest. In turn the infestation of insects has caused extensive damage to western coniferous forests. The outbreak has widespread economic and environmental implications including timber quality, water quality, fire hazard as well as releasing vast quantities of carbon into the atmosphere.

134

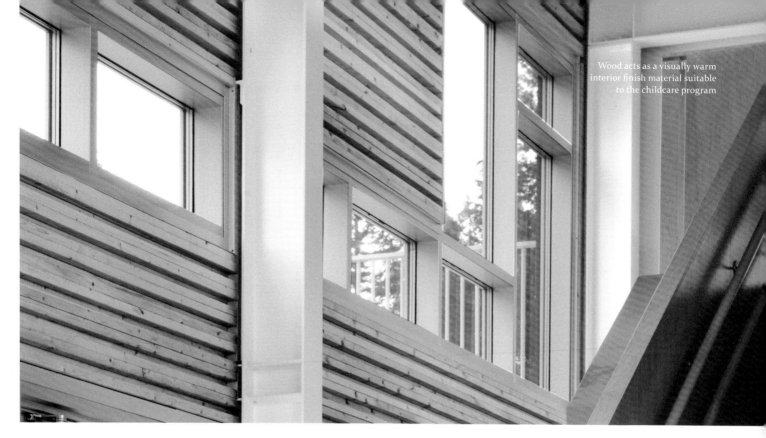

WOOD — A NATURAL FOR THE CENTRE

For timber, all wood is to be certified by the Forest Stewardship Council (FSC), whether from salvaged sources, or from the intentional harvest of timber for the purpose of clearing the particular site. However, due to the Pine Beetle epidemic that has ravaged many forests in British Columbia, the timely harvesting of compromised timber (before rotting biomass releases massive quantities of carbon, or fuels unnaturally large forest fires) presented a solution of sorts, and an opportunity for building innovation wrapped into one.

HCMA not only recognized the value of using sustainably-sourced Pine Beetle killed timber for the construction of the Centre, they viewed the situation as a great opportunity to test a simple, yet innovative, solution utilizing wood panels comprised of standard dimensional lumber as a primary component of the building's structure. The nail-laminated solid wood panels were then manually assembled on-site using a "one-2x4 + two-2x6" pattern. Not only was the assembly efficient and required no specifically-skilled labor, the innovative fabrication allowed for the concealment of electrical conduits, providing a clean interior surface within the Centre.

Utilizing beetle-kill wood to reduce the demands on healthy ecosystems (carbon sequestration and low-embodied energy) was not entirely sufficient to meet the Responsible Industry Imperative. Notwithstanding, the generous use of wood on the project contributed to its sustainability and to local and regional economies, as well as adding to the building's natural aesthetic. To fully meet the conditions of the Imperative, the team made sure to verify and document the chain of custody, also checking for compliance with sustainable forestry management practices in line with those of the FSC.

135

RECOVERED, RECLAIMED, SALVAGED AND SAVED

Spurred by demand, the ILFI published a series of Petal guides, the first of which was the Materials *Handbook* (May 2013). The first iteration of the handbook, written to support the Standard v2.1, described *Salvaged Materials* and potential applications as follows:

Salvaged Materials: The use of salvaged materials is encouraged to acknowledge the considerable value of a material's embodied energy and, typically, ingredients do not need to be tracked. However, a salvaged material cannot be used if it is known to contain a RED LIST ingredient, unless that RED LIST ingredient falls under an existing exception. If it is not obvious that the product contains a red list ingredient the team is not required to obtain an ingredients list for the salvaged product and the product is exempt from red list requirements. Advocacy is not required for salvaged materials. **MATERIALS PETAL HANDBOOK, MAY 2013, 11 RED LIST, PAGE 6**

While the Centre was officially registered for v1.3 of the Challenge and, as such, was beholden to comply with v1.3, the project team for the Centre was fully on board with adopting many of the newest advancements noted in v2.1. In effect, HCMA, the Trust, and the entire team were holding to the higher Standard.

> *"We were noticing that materials selection was beginning to have a ripple effect throughout the industry."*
>
> **JAY LIN**
> Architect, HCMA

GENERATION GREEN

136

BUILDING WITH A (RE)PURPOSE

As a regionally abundant material in the Pacific Northwest, wood was an obvious economical and sustainable solution for many applications at the UniverCity Childcare Centre. The cedar siding and fencing, header beams, millwork, and particleboards are all FSC-certified. According to HCMA, finding local sources of FSC Pure or FSC-certified products proved to be somewhat time consuming, but it also encouraged the project team to come up with even more sustainable building solutions.

A notable example of the resourceful, waste-not spirit on the building site came in the form of the repurposing of off-cuts from the FSC Pure fascia of the building. Surplus pieces of the wooden cladding were reused to construct the wastewater treatment hatch for the Centre. The benefits for the environment and the bottom line of the project did not end there. At a critical stage of construction, the project was short one pre-engineered header beam. Faced with the expensive and critical problem of procuring a new replacement, structural engineers, Fast + Epp, Ledcor staff, and the consultant team collaboratively came up with a clever solution that utilized salvaged wood to fabricate a structurally comparable beam. Such ingenuity in the form of repurposing materials are examples of the clever, sometimes on-the-fly thinking that not only mitigated construction waste and reduced costs but also resulted in some elegant design solutions.

HCMA also sourced some beautiful salvaged wood for the windowsills, mezzanine stairs and the community room stage. Outside, a large salvaged cedar root wad and the three unique, woven-wood huts on the playground were custom crafted by local artists — all original, natural and functional for recreation. A handsome outdoor bench and stage were created for the main entry from a cedar log found on-site, and while not "salvaged," furniture inside the Centre is predominantly made from wood. Timber in one form or another is utilized throughout the Centre.

IMPERATIVE:
APPROPRIATE MATERIALS/SERVICES RADIUS

**The intent of the Appropriate Materials/Services Radius Imperative
is to support regional economies and expertise, and to reduce the
environmental impacts associated with transporting people and products.
Think "heavy-near, light-far" says the ILFI's Jason F. McLennan.**

Source locations for Materials and Services must adhere to procurement zones prescribed in the Standard. Graduated zones each have a limited radius based on the Challenge's Weight/Distance prescriptions. Prohibitive costs for transporting heavy goods long distances combined with the benefits of promoting local economies underpin the zoned geographic model (see figure 1). Simply put, in current world conditions where energy is increasingly expensive, the heavier the product, the higher its cost to transport.

Step by step, HCMA's Mahvash and Lin were responsible for identifying which materials needed to be tracked, determining the zone radius allowance for each item, and ensuring that the project steered clear of any product linked, even remotely, to the Red List. Heavy, high-density products such as the I-beams that form the steel structural frame for the Centre were manufactured nearby in Vancouver's Lower Mainland. The Challenge's zone allowances for light-to-medium density materials are more lenient, taking relative transportation costs into account. Considered to be the ultimate ultra-light resources, powerful for the transformative potential, the Challenge team quips about the weighty influence of creativity and ingenuity; "Ideas can come from anywhere on the planet."

In order for the Centre to comply with this Imperative, the team had to adhere to the Challenge's prescribed Services Radius and incorporate "place-based solutions plus contribute to the expansion of a regional economy rooted in sustainable practices, products and services." The UniverCity Childcare project, for all its advantages, namely a supportive, progressive community, local design expertise and skilled local contractor, was faced with the reality of approximately half of the radius for sourcing materials and services falling in the Pacific Ocean — and another significant portion of the radius located in a natural, undeveloped and unpopulated landscape with little commerce and practically no manufacturing sector. Furthermore, the traditional manufacturing epicenter of North America was some 2,500 miles east — outside the zone allowance for many commonly used building products.

Thankfully, innovative technologies had become increasingly available on the West Coast. For example, the boundaries for sourcing renewable energy technologies such as the Centre's rooftop photovoltaic system and solar thermal array were more generous, falling within the Challenge's radius specifications.

The utilization of regionally-sourced wood and steel products, the hiring of local designers and consultants, plus the commissioning of local artists are all tangible examples of how the Centre complied with the Appropriate Materials/Services Radius Imperative.

IMPERATIVE:
LEADERSHIP IN CONSTRUCTION WASTE

Leadership in Construction Waste called for the project to divert all types of construction waste from local landfills. The Standard required that everything be reconciled by weight and then for an exceedingly high percentage of the construction waste to be recycled, reused, salvaged or composted. While Ledcor was already adept at diverting about 80 to 82 percent of construction waste on other green projects, the Challenge required an exemplary 95-plus percent diversion rate. They were tasked with the responsibility of overseeing the separating out of metals, paper and cardboard, soils and biomass, rigid foam, carpet and insulation, as well as a miscellaneous list of building materials including just about every other material one may find at a construction site including asphalt, masonry and concrete, lumber, millwork scraps, electrical refuse, fixtures of all types, HVAC components, all manner of architectural parts, wallboard and windows. Contracting a waste hauler that could deliver comprehensive services for the handling of all these materials and provide the proper documentation was critical for meeting the Imperative.

The diligent stewardship of waste continued beyond construction to the actions of every person who set foot onto the site. On breaks and during lunch personnel utilized dishes and cutlery from their own homes instead of disposables that would have added to the project's total waste. Visitors and workers alike were no longer chucking coffee cups or food scraps into the trash; rather, they were directed to separate out the organics for composting and sort the components (lids, cups, stir-sticks, etcetera) into pre-specified containers. Monitoring was required though Ledcor formulated a waste management plan that outlined the rationale and expectations, and provided it to all the trades to help facilitate the on-site behavioral shift. According to Ledcor, eighty kilograms of waste came from the project in the end.

IMPERATIVE:
CONSTRUCTION CARBON FOOTPRINT

This Imperative specifies a one-time offset of emissions tied to site development and overall construction of the project. In order to meet the Materials Petal Imperative, a thorough valuation of the UniverCity Childcare Centre's construction carbon footprint was required.

Part and parcel to addressing all aspects of the Materials Petal, HCMA and Ledcor meticulously tracked and documented all the materials used in building the UniverCity Childcare Centre. The detailed information collected was particularly useful in accounting for the carbon emissions from site/project development, construction-related activities, and for estimating the carbon contained within the Centre's building materials, sometimes referred to as "embodied construction emissions." Next, HCMA was to choose one of the three acceptable carbon calculators to fix a value for the offset. Of note, unlike most building projects, the Centre utilizes several forms of on-site renewable energy (see Energy Petal, page 102), which effectively counters a significant portion of the project's carbon emissions sum. The final step was to tally the remainder of the energy/carbon account to be reconciled and then purchase carbon offsets, formally known as Certified Emissions Reductions (CER), from a reputable third party.

View west over Burnaby Mountain to the Pacific Ocean. UniverCity, then Simon Fraser University in the foreground with the Vancouver skyline in the distance.

View down from the observation mezzanine to one of the Centre's community rooms

MATERIAL INGENUITY

**HCMA summed up the importance of the project as it related
back to the Materials Petal in a submission for a British
Columbia-based wood design award. In their words, "Being
an educational facility in an academic setting, it could not be
more appropriate that the lessons learned and the legacy of the
UniverCity Childcare project extended well beyond its users
and the immediate environment within which it is located to
include almost everybody involved in the project from local forest
stewards and mills to wood artisans, plant workers and beyond."**

In the case of mechanical and electrical systems, meeting the Materials Petal requirements were a
real barrier because every component, gasket and seal had to be evaluated for compliance. For the
trades, the Appropriate Sourcing radius was unfamiliar territory and while the Imperative appeared
simple, there was a long list of footnotes to be interpreted. To streamline the interpretive process
Ledcor created a comprehensive one-page matrix that included every specification, zone and the
distance that trades needed to know. Ledcor utilized a similar matrix in its toolkit at the Van Dusen
Garden Living Building, contributing to efficiencies on that project too. Similarly, some of the
lessons learned from challenges faced on the Van Dusen project benefited the Centre directly.

Ultimately, a thorough "Materials Tracker Matrix" was also written and submitted to the
Living Building Challenge for documentation purposes. Creating these tools went a long
way toward assisting contractors with interpreting procurement protocol, saved valuable
time on the project and generally sped up the learning curve for working within the Living
Building Standard. Ingenuity and resourcefulness are the hallmarks of the teams working on
Living Building projects and, at the UniverCity Childcare Centre, design and construction
held fast to the waste-not spirit of solutions born through the Living Building Challenge.

THE BEAUTY + INSPIRATION PETAL

Enriching Education

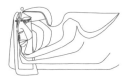

Local artist Alastair Heseltine created unique play structures by weaving long willow branches over tall tulip-shaped frames into three distinctive huts. The fantastical shelters celebrate design, and the imagination and spirit of the children attending the Childcare Centre.

145

SUMMARY OF THE LIVING BUILDING CHALLENGE VERSION 1.3 BEAUTY AND INSPIRATION PETAL

Petal Intent

Much of the contemporary built environment has devolved to unattractive, sometimes inhumane streetscapes, structures and stark landscapes, all too often denuded of natural beauty and repopulated by big box retail strip malls, agricultural monocultures, bleak industrial complexes and sterile office towers. Deteriorating transportation systems based on a near obsolescent automobile culture then connects society's sprawling developments. Apathy has led much of society to accept an uninspired formulaic suburban existence instead of opting for vibrant community living.

The Living Building Challenge recognizes the need for beauty as an essential precursor for humanity to value, preserve, conserve and serve the greater good.

Petal Imperatives
• Beauty and Spirit
• Inspiration and Education

146

"It's one of those wonderful business relationships that makes economic sense. Our green building requirements appeal to the developers for its simplicity, clarity and certainty — and gives us something that simply does not exist anywhere else in North America."

GORDON HARRIS
President and CEO, SFU Community Trust

PREDESTINED TO BE EDUCATIONAL, BEAUTIFUL AND INSPIRING

Spectacularly located at the summit of Burnaby Mountain, adjacent to academic giant Simon Fraser University and situated in the urban sweet spot of UniverCity, Canada's most progressive sustainable community, the UniverCity Childcare Centre is extraordinary. The entire mountaintop community is characterized by a pervading educational spirit and sustained by British Columbia's stunning panorama. Stylish and attractive, the elegant west coast design of the UniverCity Childcare Centre blends seamlessly within UniverCity's urban-natural setting. The well-defined architectural lines and boreal forest-inspired palette of colors fit perfectly into the mountaintop setting of the new urban village. Stepping inside the Centre, visitors experience the spirited sights and sounds of young children enthusiastically living and learning in a building that is unlike any other.

"We often see the repurposing of church basements in childcare. Having dedicated space (the Centre) is a joy."

MARGARET MACDONALD, Ph.D.
SFU Faculty of Education

KNOWLEDGE GROWS THROUGH SHARING

In order to meet the Imperatives of the Beauty and Inspiration Petal, Living Building projects are to contain design features intended solely for human delight and the celebration of culture, spirit and place appropriate to the function of the building.

Further, educational materials detailing performance and operations of the building are to be publicly available with the intent that the sharing of innovative solutions will help to inform and motivate others to make change. Lastly, the building must be open to the public at least one day per year to facilitate direct exposure to a Living Building.

IMPERATIVE:
BEAUTY AND SPIRIT

Valuing cultural identity and aesthetics, and the characteristic benefits that art and creativity in any form contribute to architecture, design team members fostered partnerships with local British Columbia artists to bring Beauty, Spirit and Inspiration to the UniverCity Childcare Centre project.

Renowned mixed-media sculptor Alastair Heseltine of Hornby Island created unique play structures for the children by weaving long willow branches over tall tulip-shaped frames into three distinctive huts of varying sizes. The fantastical shelters have a single entryway much like other iconic structures such as teepees, igloos and tents. The woven willow huts, effectively celebrating design, and the imagination and spirit of children, occupy an upper location on the playground. Designed by space2place, a series of playful stepping-stones of varying heights mark the approach to the whimsical huts with a giant rope nest located in the vicinity. Adding to the dynamic playful nature of the site is the varying landscape elevations that invite children to climb up and jump down. Weaving paths, ramps, stone steps and an impressive giant silver slide connect all of the different attractions and lookout points while inviting the children to freely explore the Centre's grounds and playful art forms.

Professional sculptor Warren Brubacher from Squamish specializes in reclaiming twisted wood pieces from the forest floor of British Columbia's coastal rainforests and creatively repurposes his finds into functional, natural art such as outdoor benches and furniture. Brubacher salvaged, then finished and installed the impressive large gnarled Western Red Cedar root wad present in the playground. The beautifully simple stump climbing structure (inverted roots up) immediately draws the attention of everyone who visits the Centre and it is equally powerful for its value as a play experience for the children. While the simplicity is compelling, the provision of such a natural climbing element was a challenge to implement, with careful shaping and sanding needed to ensure that the structure met all Canadian Standards and Health Authority approval for child play in regard to height, size of openings, and other elements not typically integrated into such an installation.

Yet another local craftsman, Brent Comber, creates functional pieces from cast-off wood ends sourced from various timber mills and lumberyards around British Columbia. Comber added to the hands-on collection of local art at the Centre, fashioning a handsome outdoor bench from recouped cedar. This place of play, rest, and engagement is particularly compelling, as it was salvaged from the site itself, and re-purposed as an element of welcoming. Each beautiful feature and its accompanying environmental story add to the enjoyment, education, and culture of the Childcare Centre.

Within the building itself, children, parents, and visitors alike are greeted by a beautiful atrium with double-height windows soaring to the roof. This light-filled atrium celebrates transparency and warmth, and has been dubbed "the beach" by the children who lie on its warm, sun-drenched floors on cool winter days. The experience of the atrium is enhanced by the creative translucent window art based on a photograph taken by Nathan Chow of HCMA. Joel Berman Glass Studios International then printed the imagery onto the glass pieces with the glazing contractor then installing the glass. This series of dandelions represents the Living Building Challenge and the notion of the seedpod cast upon the wind to share the knowledge that is learned within this Centre to the greater community.

Further to this feature, as the children gaze skyward in the dwindling light of day, they see three beautiful light fixtures, custom designed by local artists, Propeller Designs. The lights are orb-like and at once represent the sun, the moon, the sky... but most of all, simplicity and transparency. They are art as much as they are function, but they are not intended to dominate the space, rather to simply exist in the open environment of the atrium providing backlighting to the dandelion windows as they explode even further at night.

IMPERATIVE:
INSPIRATION AND EDUCATION

Begin with Joy. Joy, freedom, respect, exploration, experience, discovery. These core values are embedded in the thoughtful architecture of the building and its delightful outdoor spaces.

"The outdoors is full of joy because it is not prescriptive like traditional playgrounds. There is challenge, and interest, and curiosity in the elements that the children can use as they see fit," says early-childhood education expert Patricia Frouws. The recreational elements created by the design team are certainly innovative by today's standards. The ecologically-minded landscape architecture firm space2place steadfastly honored nature in their design, acknowledging the Centre's educational programming by facilitating opportunities for creative interactions with natural materials like wood, stone, water and sand as timeless means to play.

Through play, young children observe and experiment — they learn by doing. And the use of basic, natural materials is time tested. For example, the beautiful, reclaimed Western Red Cedar root wad stands as one of a number of exquisite focal points in the outdoor space immediately adjacent to the building — a natural climbing apparatus and a material extension of a natural forest. The surrounding sandpit and water features (see Waterplay) around the outdoor play space are magnets to young troupes searching for fun. Through nature-based recreation, children unconsciously experience the fundamentals of such heady disciplines as physics, engineering and hydrodynamics, simply by manipulating the flow of water and sculpting sand with whatever implements and natural objects that may be at hand. The principles of gravity, and tangible aspects of the water cycle for that matter, can be observed as rainwater cascades down the rain chain or experienced while descending

the slide or scooting around on a tricycle. Organic learning is integrated into the opportunities for discovery found everywhere at the Centre — and from the point of view of the educators, parents and designers, the more hands-on experiences that are available, the more delight there is in learning.

Program Director Karen Vaughan (who also teaches child psychology outside of the Centre) notes that "children learn holistically," remarking that "the opportunities for development in the social, physical, cognitive, and emotional domains are intertwined here at the Centre." A freer form of play that promotes both motor skill development and exploration (cognitive and physical) is encouraged by educators and facilitated through Reggio Emilia and instilled in the Living Building design. Children can move to outdoor spaces freely — building, shaping, climbing, clambering, splashing, plunging, and rolling — learning all the while.

Addressing transparency and how the expansive knee-to-ceiling windows accommodate child-sized sightlines for the Centre's young occupants, Karen Vaughan notes that the children enjoy playing with the varying light. "When the sun streams in, the children delight in playing with the stripes and shadows cast by the beams and by their own movement." The design team approached transparency sincerely, ensuring that there were robust indoor-indoor, indoor-outdoor and outdoor-outdoor connections so that the children and educators continually have a sense of what is going on in their world.

"This is the most beautiful building I have ever been in, as far as a childcare facility is concerned. It's gorgeous. I love it completely, everything about the design and the light."

MARGARET MACDONALD, Ph.D.
SFU Faculty of Education

"There's a beautiful relationship between the indoor and the outdoor spaces."

PATRICIA FROUWS
Executive Director,
SFU Childcare Society

WATERPLAY — NOURISHING THE SENSES

Touch, Sight, Smell, Sound, Taste. The educational tenets in place at the UniverCity Childcare Centre are underpinned by opportunities for personal discovery.

Embracing "discovery" as both a design principle and educational approach, the team integrated several distinct, hands-on water features around the Centre's grounds. Educators and the design team were invested in employing experiential elements at the Centre that held true potential to engage the children in imaginative and educational play.

A constructed, functional fluvial rill, shaped in a Fibonacci-like arc around a landscaped slope and the Centre's sandpit, channels rainwater alongside a pathway down to an infiltration gallery. The slender, 70 metre-long, 400 mm wide canal streams water intermittently, offering occasions for exploratory play where leaves, pine needles and walnut shells make for excellent little boats for floating and racing.

When precipitation runoff is not adequate to charge the rill naturally, children can add water themselves by opening the colorful, child-sized diversion valve—a "steering wheel" attached to a guardrail located next to the building on the rooftop deck that is both a functional device and an educational tool. Through this design feature, water stored in a small rainwater catchment can be directed into a scupper on the roof. Then, by operating the manual diversion valve, children can control the water flow and bring the watercourse to life. The nearby British Columbia Institute of Technology (BCIT) was commissioned to create the custom plumbing fixture and while it may not qualify as art, the interactive water diverter is innovative and fun. Based on the excited reactions of the children playing with the water feature, the rill and the diversion valve get full marks for inspiring discovery.

"The aesthetics of the building were supported by the principles of the Living Building Challenge."

KOUROSH MAHVASH
Sustainable Research Leader, HCMA

"Quite simply, when we deny our children nature, we deny them beauty."

RICHARD LOUV,
Last Child in the Woods

153

GENERATION GREEN

FORMS THAT MIMIC NATURE

According to landscape architects space2place, "the main challenge of this project was to meet the rigorous Living Building Challenge criteria and provide an innovative amenity built with locally-sourced and non-toxic materials." Beyond meeting the Imperatives of the Challenge, HCMA and space2place focused on finding ways to honor the children in the design by incorporating elements in harmony with the Reggio Emilia methodology that spurred creativity, curiosity and imagination.

In a project description space2place summed up the integrated approach to the UniverCity Childcare Centre Living Building:

"Rejecting catalogue-based play equipment, we invited local daycare children to help us re-imagine play spaces and we collaborated with local artisans to develop unique play features. The site provides children with a diverse range of creative, physical and social forms of play — a space where children can create their own experiments and performances."

The commitment to the integrated design process of the entire team proved to be key for meeting the Challenge Imperatives and the educational goals.

155

PART IV

Conclusion

Doing the Right Thing

157

"We stumbled upon the Living Building Challenge and thought, what if? What if these children could spend three years of their lives resetting their normal — expecting that we treat and re-use our rainwater, expecting that we generate the energy we need, expecting that you can inhabit the building and not get sick, expecting that the building will still be there for their children and their grandchildren."

DALE MIKKELSEN
Director of Development, SFU Community Trust

LIVING LABORATORY

Deep green sustainability has been embraced by SFU and implemented by the team at the SFU Community Trust. As a result, UniverCity has effectively become a living, growing testing ground for the most innovative urban concepts, energy systems and building designs necessary for the creation of an ecologically robust and economically sustainable community. The community's clear goals and dedicated strategy for implementation, catalyzed by the leadership's healthy disregard for the status quo, has led to an ongoing stream of laurels, successes and firsts.

There is no doubt that smart development decisions have been the foundation for, and supported the success of, the UniverCity Childcare Centre in terms of its involvement with the Living Building Challenge. The Living Building Challenge's scale jumping platform is perfectly suited to making the most of the entire community setting so that resources can be shared building to building and true cost effective sustainable solutions can benefit everyone. For the Centre, the green attributes of UniverCity led to a number of opportunities to scale jump the Imperatives tied to the Energy Petal, the Site Petal and the Water Petal.

By implementing a Neighborhood Energy Utility, UniverCity will quickly become Canada's largest neighborhood utility. More importantly, the shared utility operation reduces greenhouse gasses by more than 50 percent and without it the Centre would not have had a cost-effective solution for net zero energy. An added advantage is that other buildings in the community also benefit from the communal energy source.

In terms of maintaining the natural ecology of place, the UniverCity Childcare Centre went beyond the current requirements of the Living Building Challenge. The Centre was also one of many buildings benefiting from the community's inclusive stormwater management system engineered to maintain pre-development stormwater runoff quality and quantity. Director of Development Dale Mikkelsen firmly believes that the sustainable community foundation made the UniverCity Childcare Centre Living Building both possible and affordable. Further, Mikkelsen believes that building more community-based sustainable infrastructure is a springboard for exploring the reality of Living Neighborhoods. Creating Living Buildings on Burnaby Mountain is possible because sustainable synergies are part of UniverCity's DNA.

"Scale jumping is an important part of the message because we would like to see more community level infrastructure being built in order to more successfully replicate Living Buildings."

DALE MIKKELSEN
Director of Development,
SFU Community Trust

"SFU Childcare Society values children as the heart of our respectful, collaborative and reflective community by providing them with a place to develop their potential through freedom to explore and engage the world around them."

**SFU CHILDCARE SOCIETY
VISION STATEMENT**

EDUCATION FOR ALL

The UniverCity Childcare Centre Living Building truly represents a higher ground for design and learning. UniverCity's achievements are predicated by SFU's strategic vision to establish the institution as Canada's most community-engaged research university.

With the social, economic, environmental and cultural well-being of the community foremost in its outlook, it was a natural step for the Trust to increase its sustainability initiatives by aiming to construct one of Canada's very first Living Buildings. While the purpose of education is clear and omnipresent on a university campus, honoring 3 to 5 year old members of this type of community with the best facility and best education is novel. Also noteworthy as an important, albeit unintended, consequence of this project is the value-added learning and professional development for the planners, design practitioners and ancillary services people, as well as company and organization personnel who had a connection to the UniverCity Childcare Centre Living Building project. The Centre's design team members are the first to say that the process of creating a Living Building requires more time, more research, more inclusiveness and presents more challenges than other standard types of buildings but it is tremendously rewarding. Participating in a Living Building Challenge project positively changes the culture of how design is done – and the rewards come in the form of incredible learning experiences and a sense of pride and empowerment from start to finish.

COMMUNICATING, LEARNING, EVOLVING, CREATING

In order to achieve the best possible outcome, the entire design team had to be (and wanted to be) much more inclusive with all project stakeholders and invest more time than ever previously experienced to conduct an extraordinary amount of research.

The value of sharing protocols and information across projects was acknowledged by the Trust, Ledcor and the design team. After all, gleaning knowledge from discoveries on other Living Building projects could very well mean the difference between extra days or weeks for research, costly design revisions, or construction delays. The significance of sharing information across Living Building teams, disciplines and projects is, in fact, emblematic of the collaborative spirit of the leading edge of the sustainability and environmental movement.

Understanding the particulars of the building's operation and the rationale behind certain design attributes was critical for the building to function as it was intended. In a testament to the project's inclusivity principle and their professional investment in the project, HCMA arranged meetings with the Childcare Centre's users to gather valuable insights into what they envisioned in the new building and to explain the significant differences between the Centre functioning as a Living Building compared to a traditional facility.

Design team members listened to the children's wishes and the educator's input intently, extracting design attributes out of their messages that best complemented learning and joy. The resulting design now offers endless opportunities for delight and discovery, uniting play and education elegantly into the Childcare Centre. Children attending the UniverCity Childcare Centre are getting a world-class education in a world-class building, in a world-class community.

SERVING AS A BRIDGE

Capable and motivated, the Trust's actions serve as an effective bridge for creating leading-edge community development that reconciles the built environment with its natural surroundings.

Similarly, the Living Building Challenge is a cutting-edge advocacy structure conceived to challenge the design and construction industries as well as government bodies and community citizens to create sustainable, resilient, and equitable communities while valuing local and global biodiversity.

The Trust leadership is to be commended for supporting the remarkable parallels between the Living Building Challenge philosophy and the Reggio Emilia early childhood education philosophy. SFU Childcare Society Executive Director Patricia Frouws sincerely sums up the pervading attitude of everyone involved in bringing the Centre to

fruition; "My mind and heart are continually focused on providing the best for the children in our care. As society continues to evolve in many areas, so does our thinking about how children learn, and our respect for the way they understand the world." The commitment of the entire SFU community to advancing education, signified by the bold decisions to implement a unique early childhood education approach and to pursue Living Building Challenge certification for the UniverCity Childcare Centre is a noteworthy marker of where environmental sustainability blends seamlessly with economic and social sustainability.

ENVIRONMENT + ECONOMY

A central theme of the extraordinary story of achievements unfolding on Burnaby Mountain is the powerful vision of the SFU Community Trust for a sustainable presence.

Undaunted by the current preconception of a "green building premium" associated with designing and constructing high-performance green buildings, the Trust has proven itself as a remarkably unique kind of developer by holding itself accountable to the highest environmental standards while adhering to the principles of sound economics. Operating as a master planner and developer, the Trust has never lost sight of its mandate to create a model sustainable community while contributing endowment wealth to support teaching and research at Simon Fraser University. UniverCity with its considerable assets, and the Trust with its impassioned vision for true

sustainability, together give rise to an incredibly fertile place for creating a Living Building. The economic reality that the UniverCity Childcare Centre Living Building was constructed for less than comparable, conventionally built childcare facilities is evidence that what many people had envisioned to be the future of sustainable design is absolutely possible now. It is both remarkable and rewarding to see that achieving the highest levels of sustainable design makes sound economic sense as demonstrated by the UniverCity Childcare Centre.

LIVING LEGACY

Imagine what society could be like if the world's future leaders spent their formative years inhabiting Living Buildings that were purposely designed to honor early childhood development, respecting the ways children understand the world, and by providing opportunities for discovery and delight. Imagine schools where playing and learning with nature in mind was encouraged through a unique curriculum approach that teaches children about true sustainability. Imagine all children being surrounded by educators, families and communities where the regeneration of the planet, caring for the environment, and appreciating nature as a valuable teacher is accepted as standard.

All of these imaginations have transformed to reality and are actually happening now at the UniverCity Childcare Centre Living Building.

The UniverCity Childcare Centre Living Building is standing proof of the visionary conviction of a small, but growing, group of people dedicated to doing the right thing for the betterment of humanity and the natural world. The implications of such a profound, shared vision cannot be understated. Their collective foresight and labor has established a regenerative path to the future that runs through UniverCity. The legacy of all the children from the UniverCity Childcare Centre will be found on that regenerative path.

APPENDIX: AWARDS AND RECOGNITION

UNIVERCITY AND UNIVERCITY CHILDCARE AWARDS

2013 Quality Urban Energy Systems of Tomorrow
QUEST Community Energy Builder Award

2013 Canadian Society Landscape Architects
Award of Excellence - UniverCity Childcare Centre

2013 FortisBC Award for Excellence in Energy Efficiency
New Construction for Origin

2013 CaGBC National Leadership Awards
Green Building Champion Award - UniverCity Childcare Centre

2013 Greater Vancouver Home Builders' Association
Ovation Award - Best Multi-Family Lowrise Development for Origin

2013 Greater Vancouver Home Builders' Association
Ovation Award - Excellence in Energy Efficiency in New Construction: Multi-Family for Origin

2012 Vancouver Regional Construction Association
Silver Award of Excellence Sustainable Construction - UniverCity Childcare Centre

2012 City of Burnaby
Environment Award for Planning and Development - UniverCity Childcare Centre

2012 Urban Development Institute
Award for Excellence in Urban Development Best Sustainable - UniverCity Childcare Centre

2012 Planning Institute of British Columbia
Award of Excellence for UniverCity Phase 3 Masterplan & Zoning

2011 Canadian Institute of Planners
Award for Planning Excellence: Neighbourhood Planning

2011 Federation of Canadian Municipalities
Sustainable Communities Award for Integrated Neighbourhood Development

2009 Urban Land Institute
Award for Excellence: The Americas for Best Practice in Design, Architecture and Development

2008 CMHC
Best Practices in Affordable Housing Award for the Verdant @ UniverCity

2008 LivCom Awards
Gold Award and third place-ranking overall in the Sustainable Projects Category

2008 City of Burnaby
Environment Award for Planning and Development for the Verdant @ UniverCity

2008 American Planning Association
National Excellence Award for Innovation in Green Community Planning

2007 Urban Development Institute
Award for Innovations in Creating a More Livable & Sustainable Region

2007 Urban Development Institute
Award to the Verdant @ UniverCity for Innovations in Creating More Sustainable Development

2007 Urban Development Institute
Award to the Verdant @ UniverCity for Innovations in Creating More Affordable Housing

2007 City of Burnaby
Environment Award for Planning and Development

2006 Planning Institute of British Columbia
Award of Excellence for Site Planning and Design

2005 Canadian Home Builders' Association
SAM Award for Best Community Development in Canada

2005 Canadian Home Builders' Association
Georgie Award to The Cornerstone for Best Environmental Consideration and Energy Efficiency

2005 Association of University Real Estate Officials (AUREO)
Award of Excellence

2005 City of Burnaby
Environment Award for Planning and Development for The Cornerstone

2005 Urban Development Institute
Award for Excellence in Urban Development for the Cornerstone

2005 Burnaby Board of Trade
Newsmaker of the Year Award

2005 BC Hydro Power Smart Excellence Award
Residential Building Developer for The Cornerstone

LIVING BUILDING PARTNERS

ORGANIZATIONS

SFU Community Trust (Owner/developer)

Simon Fraser University

SFU Faculty of Education

SFU Childcare Society

International Living Future Institute

Cascadia Green Building Council

Canada Green Building Council

DESIGN TEAM

Architect: Hughes Condon Marler Architects

Structural Engineer: Fast + Epp Structural Engineers

Landscape Architect: space2place Landscape Architects

Civil Engineer: AECOM

Mechanical Engineer: Integral Group

Electrical Engineer: MMM Group

GENERAL CONTRACTOR

Ledcor Construction

SUB-CONTRACTORS

Lockerbie and Hole Mechanical

ECOfluid Systems Inc.

North by North West Landscaping

Korda Painting and Decorating

Colossus Drywall

Wanes Custom Woodworks Inc.

PHOTO AND DIAGRAM CREDITS

All photos by Martin Tessler except as noted:

SFU Community Trust: pages 9, 10–11, 12–17, 19–25, 32–33, 82-83, 140–141

Hughes Condon Marler Architects: pages 44, 79, 81, 90, 92, 95, 98, 109

iStock: pages 86–89, 134

ECOfluid Systems Inc.: page 99

INTERNATIONAL
LIVING FUTURE INSTITUTE

The International Living Future Institute is an environmental NGO committed to catalyzing the transformation toward communities that are socially just, culturally rich and ecologically restorative. The Institute is premised on the belief that providing a compelling vision for the future is a fundamental requirement for reconciling humanity's relationship with the natural world. The Institute operates the Living Building Challenge, the built environment's most rigorous performance standard, and Declare, an ingredients label for building materials. It houses the Cascadia Green Building Council and Ecotone Publishing.

ECOTONE PUBLISHING

Founded by green building experts in 2004, Ecotone Publishing is dedicated to meeting the growing demand for authoritative and accessible books on sustainable design, materials selection and building techniques in North America and beyond. Located in the Cascadia region, Ecotone is well positioned to play an important part in the green design movement. Ecotone searches out and documents inspiring projects, visionary people and vital trends that are leading the design industry to transformational change toward a healthier planet.

LIVING BUILDING CHALLENGE

The Living Building Challenge is the built environment's most rigorous performance standard. It calls for the creation of building projects at all scales that operate as cleanly, beautifully and efficiently as nature's architecture. To be certified under the Challenge, projects must meet a series of ambitious performance requirements, including net zero energy, waste and water, over a minimum of 12 months of continuous occupancy.